THE FEEL GOOD FACTORY ON

great sex

THE FEEL GOOD FACTORY ON

great sex

mind-blowing,
earth-moving,
pulse-racing secrets
to spice up your love life

Feel Good Factory led by Elisabeth Wilson

MANUFACTURED BY
THE FEEL GOOD FACTORY

First published in 2009 by
Infinite Ideas Limited
36 St Giles
Oxford
OX1 3LD
United Kingdom
www.infideas.com

A CIP catalogue record for this book is available from the British Library.

ISBN 978–1–906821–21–0

The publisher would like to thank Marcelle Perks, Helena Frith-Powell and
Elisabeth Wilson for their contributions to this book.

Designed by D.R.ink
Typeset by Nicki Averill
Printed and bound in Malta

Contents

One: Look at you
Because the most important element in improving your sex life is tuning in and turning on to yourself.

Two: Communicate, connect... and it's not all about talking

Whatever helps you connect will help your love life – and that doesn't always mean talking.

Three: Just like the first time
Want to get the thrill back? Here are some ideas that work.

Four: Making a good thing better
Because there's always room for a little improvement

Introduction

Do you feel your sex life could be taken to a new level? There are some quick, reliable and above all easy ways to reignite the fire. For sex advice to work, you must act upon it rather than simply read about it, however – and that's far more likely if it's not too intimidating or difficult.

Most of us can't just go back to the teenage years when sex was the focus of our attention because life is just too busy now but we could give our love life a little more attention than it's getting at the moment – and that may be all it takes.

You probably know most of what is written here, but what is odd is how quickly we 'forget' what we know. Just following the very straightforward ideas for improving your sexual confidence will do your sex life untold good. And by improving communication, as recommended in the second section, you'll see another huge leap. It doesn't take a lot to get you talking to each other again about what you like and also what you don't like. Then there are a couple of sections to get you moving towards a more fulfilling sex life. At the

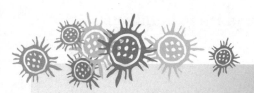

Feel good now: *Throw in an element of surprise: do something slightly different to the last time, each time you make love. After a few weeks, mixing things up becomes second nature and the pay-off will make it worthwhile.*

very least, these ideas can give you a great laugh when things go wrong and can blow your socks off when they go right.

To quote the famous sex novelist Erica Jong: 'There are things that happen in the dark between two people that make everything that happens in the light all right.' With very little effort, you can greatly improve your sex life. And that's going to make everything else in your life work better.

With very little effort, you can greatly improve your sex life

One
Look at you

Because the most important element in improving your sex life is tuning in and turning on to yourself.

Body perfect?

Insecurity eats away at desire. Don't let pictures of the beautiful and famous make you feel inadequate. The top performers, models and stars probably feel less confident than you do.

Beautiful women are frequently held up as an ideal
and yet celebrities suffer more than you might think.
They may seem to have it all – looks, public adoration,
money – but the cult of celebrity often makes them more
insecure. Even the most stunning women can
have problems feeling confident.

Halle Berry is a former Miss Teen All America, was the
runner-up to Miss USA and has been voted into *People*
magazine's Most Beautiful People list nine times: oh, and
she's also an Oscar winner. Despite all this, she recently
announced that she is very insecure about both her physical
appearance and her acting. On Femalefirst.com she said,
about those who pay her compliments: 'If they really knew
me, they'd realise I'm far from secure about my looks.'

Knowing that such a successful, talented and good-looking
woman is plagued by self-doubt should convince you
that beauty is only skin-deep. There's no point in thinking
that you would feel/be sexier if you looked differently;
confidence comes from within.

Similarly, Madonna, who is perhaps the most media-savvy
female performer ever, has admitted, 'I think my biggest
flaw is my insecurity… I'm plagued with insecurities 24-7.'

In *Madonna: An Intimate Biography*, J. Randy Taraborrelli
quotes dancer Sallim Gauwloos, who appeared in the
movie *In Bed with Madonna*: 'She was very, very insecure,
especially with other women. We would have parties, and
there would never be beautiful women invited. Only guys.
She would freak out if there was someone in the room more
beautiful than her.' Clearly, public persona and how stars
really feel are two different things. Lesson learned – the
grass is not always greener on the other side.

Many regular women feel intimidated when they see
airbrushed, 'perfect' images of women in the media. One
survey found only 3% of women are happy with their size
and 25% of all women in the UK are on a diet at any one
time, although around half of them are not even clinically
overweight (*Daily Mail*, 2003).

We are obsessed with how we look and all this angst is
a terrible burden on our sex lives. In *Hot Monogamy* Dr
Patricia Love uses research that shows women who have a
negative body image are 'less interested in making love…
more restricted in their range of sexual activities, and have
more difficulty becoming aroused and reaching orgasm'.

In the 1950s models weighed 8% less than the average woman, whereas in the 1990s models weighed 23% less, which makes them thinner than 95% of people. The difference between the ideal and the reality has never been further apart. Today there's much more focus on how we look: people pierce and tattoo their bodies, sculpt them with exercise and turn increasingly to cosmetic surgery. All of this is great if it makes you feel confident and empowered, but if you still feel insecure perhaps the answer is to start from the inside and work out.

So the message is: you need to feel sexy to have a better love life. Just think: if you transferred a little of the energy you put into improving your looks into feeling good about yourself and focused instead on improving your love life, the results could be quite transforming.

Only 3% of women are happy with their size

Boosting your sexual confidence

So, what is sexual confidence and how do you get your hands on some of it? If you're uptight about sex, insecure about your body or just plain worried that you're not very good at it, then building up your sexual confidence is a prerequisite to enjoying yourself.

What factor most affects your ability to have a brilliant sex life? A great body? A fabulous lover? A bendy body? If you have all of them, bully for you! Even so, without one all-important element, your love life is still likely to be ho-hum rather than fantastic: you must have sexual confidence too.

What might work

If you're feeling more than a little lacklustre about your appearance, it's very unlikely that you're enjoying a great sex life. Forget cherchez la femme (or cherchez l'homme for that matter): it's more a case of cherchez le diet.

Note: A dramatic weight loss in a long-term partner should always be viewed with terrific suspicion. If your lover loses several kilos and your sex life is less than sparkling, remember their sexual confidence is about to go sky-high and when that happens, thrilling sex is never far away… with or without you. On the other hand, if you've been feeling less like sex and you have put on a little weight, ask yourself whether being 5 kg lighter would make a difference to your libido. If it would, then diet. With a little willpower, it's by far the simplest and quickest way to feel sexually confident, but not if the problem is deeper than weight gain. If you know in your heart that you are not overweight and losing a few pounds won't give you the boost you need, you'll have to look deeper.

Perhaps you think you will feel sexier if you have surgery for bigger breasts or thinner thighs but beware: your goal is sexual confidence. If it's your partner who wants you to have surgery, you won't gain sexual confidence. And if you've had a boob job already, will having smoother thighs make all the difference?

Just like worrying that you're overweight when you're not, these are simply distractions and it's your relationship with either your partner or yourself that needs work. Spend your money on therapy or a self-esteem course instead to change your perception of yourself. Do whatever it takes to feel as attractive as you can.

• Start talking yourself up: 'I'm happy', 'I look great', 'I'm gorgeous'. Repeat these affirmations twenty times whenever you think of it.

Feel good now: *Work on feeling more sexual every day: think of yourself as a powerfully sensuous person, look for opportunities to make life more sensual, flirt…*

- Spend as much time as you can naked. This reacquaints you with your body and puts you in touch with your sexual self. As Dr Phil McGraw writes in *O, The Oprah Magazine*: 'If you're one of those people who can't even look in the mirror naked, you need to get used to it. Maybe you need to start with underwear. Maybe you need to start with a Parka, and work down from there. The point is… you're going to have to get comfortable in your own skin.'

- Devote an hour a week to loving your body. If pampering with creams and potions isn't you, start exercising or go to a massage therapist or reflexologist. Anything that gets you back in touch with that thing you need for sex – your body.

Start right now

If you were thinner, how would you behave? What would you be doing? Exercising, eating healthily, buying nice clothes? OK, so how can you start doing all those things tomorrow? The mistake most would-be slimmers make is to think in abstract rather than concrete terms and to be too ambitious. Of course you can start exercising tomorrow but it's highly unlikely you'll begin by jogging round the park four days a week, which is probably the unrealistic goal you've set yourself. It's also unrealistic to think that you might give up chocolate and crisps overnight, but you could aim to eat fruit or vegetables at every meal. Try buying one nice item of clothing, even if it's in a bigger size – this will make you feel better about yourself. Build up until you're following the sort of lifestyle that will mean you reach your goals.

Devote an hour a week to loving your body

To wax, or not to wax?

Now for the nitty-gritty essentials of personal
hygiene. Hair or not? Remember it's simply
a matter of fashion. New York women were
instrumental in taking the Brazilian wax
mainstream. Now, at the time of writing, they
are celebrating the 'full bush' look with relish
and so this really is a matter of personal taste.
The jury's out on whether it's better sexually for
your bush to be *au naturel* or not. Whatever you
do, do it to increase your sexual confidence and
to boost your body image.

Some people prefer pubic hair, others do not. The writer Mil Millington has argued fiercely that we should ban the Brazilian wax: 'Aesthetically, very few things are less appealing than the plucked-chicken-flesh look of barren genitals.' Alternatively, sex educator Violet Blue argues in favour of shaving: 'For many of us the result was an unforgettable feeling of silky-smooth skin, sensitive to the touch, with all of the bare skin's nerve endings at full attention.'

The way we present ourselves celebrates our diversity. Removing hair, or colouring it, is an easy way to do this. Use a pair of nail scissors for an overall trim if you don't actually wish to remove any hair. If you want to depilate for a V-shape, however, you might consider the common methods: a bikini-line wax, shaving or a depilation cream. It's best to have waxing professionally done at a salon but you will need at least six weeks' growth. This is a painful process (avoid when you are premenstrual and feel pain more intensely), but your skin will be smooth for around four weeks.

After waxing, avoid taking a bath or shower and exfoliate with a loofah or body scrub every few days to prevent a rash as the hairs start to come back. Those with slow

hair growth might consider depilatory creams, especially
for the bikini area. These are also good when waxing is
growing out and you are in between stages. You'll need to
leave the cream on for around 10 minutes (but follow the
instructions on the packet) and won't be able to use soap
in the area straightaway (also not recommended just before
he goes down on you!). Shaving is quickest, but all methods
can result in prickly regrowth.

To remove more of the hair (or even the whole lot), try a
Brazilian wax. This is best done at a speciality salon; it will
take around half an hour and all the parts of your vulva
(as well as your anus) will be waxed. Afterwards you can
have the area decorated with Swarovski crystals – tiny gems
with adhesive backs. Alternatively, use temporary tattoos.

You can also shave yourself at home. It's best to soften
the hair first by having a bath, or placing a wet cloth over
it. Use conditioner on your pubic hair to pre-soften, then
cut the hair short with scissors or use an electric beard
trimmer. (First-timers might want to try an overall trim
first to see how it feels – I promise this will not prickle the
skin!) It's important to sit or lie near a mirror so you can
see what you're doing. Use shaving cream and shave in the
direction in which the hair grows. You can use disposable

razors (you'll need two to four razors for this) – you might even get turned on!

Have ready a little bowl of water to dip the razor into after every stroke. Use a towel to wipe away excess foam so you can see what you are doing. On tricky areas use both hands to hold the skin taut, or ask your partner to help you and make this an erotic experience. Taking all the hair off requires practice.

Violet Blue says that shaving your butt is difficult because you can't see it yourself. She suggests 'turning around and bending over completely, so you're looking through your

Feel good now: *Don't forget to look in a mirror! As we get older or busier, we spend less time looking at our own reflection and often we try to pretend our body just isn't there. It's a mistake. Buy a full-length mirror and study yourself naked. Look at yourself dressed too and spend time preening.*

legs at your butt in the mirror, and use your free hand to pull your buttocks aside'. Use a soothing cream or zinc oxide lotion afterwards.

Other methods include laser surgery (which needs repeated sessions), sugaring and threading. Ask your beautician about these. Some people choose to show off their handiwork with a tattoo or genital piercing. You can also dye the pubic hair with henna and cut it into shapes. If it feels good, flaunt it.

Don't be concerned if you think you look odd or 'different' down there. Too many of us worry about not being the norm (porn models are routinely altered with cosmetic surgery or photoshopped to appear uniform). Take a mirror and spend some time looking at yourself. Sex educators Betty Dodson and Carlin Ross have a gallery of genitalia on their website: www.dodsonandross.com.

If it feels good, flaunt it

Tone up what matters

Strengthening your PC muscles increases arousal rate, sensations and stamina. The technique has also inspired a range of fun toys such as the vaginal barbell – a much more exciting form of home gym!

Any exercise is good for your sex life, but the optimum way to achieve better orgasms is to strengthen and tighten your pelvic floor – the actual muscles that do the most work during sex. This is the group of six muscles that control and hold in place all the holes in that area: the urethra, vagina and anus. In modern life we sit rather than squat and so these muscles are often weakened. Regular 'love squeezes' tighten and tone the muscles, a sure-fire way to put the zip back into your love life!

But pelvic exercises are not a new idea. As far back as 800 BC, Chinese texts extolled the virtues of a woman having a firm grip. In Ancient Japan *Ben Wa* balls (which give the wearer pleasurable sensations) were invented by an unknown courtesan – they also improve the grip of the PC muscles. You've probably heard of Kegel exercises. They were designed to offset the problems of urinary incontinence, especially in pregnant women, but the bonus side effect is a tightened, toned vagina. Dr Joshua Davies first suggested using the exercises, but it was Dr Arnold Kegel who popularised them.

The best way to find your PCs is to place a finger inside your vagina and clench your muscles firmly. You should be able to feel pressure on your finger. Often we use the wrong

muscles, so have a few tries until you feel something.
If you're having difficulty, add more fingers or a dildo.
Once you've located your muscles, clench them firmly and
then try to clench your anus, vagina and urethra muscles
separately. Clench and release. Try to do ten contractions, have
a rest and then go for ten more. Breathe evenly throughout.
Once you've got the hang of this, aim to complete these
exercises every day or as often as you can manage it.

About a third of all women have weak pelvic floors so that
means a lot of us quite literally have room for improvement.
Dr Kegel suggests you need to squeeze your PC muscles
30–100 times each day, but in *The 7 Minute Sex Secret*
fitness expert Martica Heaner says this is not enough to
enhance your sex life: 'You need to train for sex. You must
practise the exercises in such a way that they replicate the
rhythms, body positions and forces present during sex.'

Feel good now: *Give to charity any garments
that don't make you feel great and look fabulous.
If that leaves you with only three items of clothing,
so be it!*

She suggests you need to squeeze harder (or longer), or use some form of resistance such as vaginal barbells. Women have two types of muscles – slow and fast twitch – and we must exercise both types to get results. This is why you should alternate between power squeezes and quick flutters.

It's actually been proven that using some form of resistance (a dildo or vaginal barbell) is three times faster at getting results. The vaginal barbell is a special kind of dildo specially designed for PC exercises, although you can substitute a regular dildo if you prefer. Dr Dodson's Exercise Wand is made of stainless steel and will change angle when you contract the pelvic muscles so you know you are doing them correctly. Similarly, the Vielle Pelvic Floor Toning System has a patented locator for correct positioning and an indicator to ensure you use the right muscles.

An alternative is the Vaginal Exercise Egg. Practise with it first lying down, but when your muscles become stronger you can walk around with it. Advanced users may tie weights to the string for greater resistance training. Alternate between fast, slow and weighted clenches – or even better, check out your clenching skills during sex with your partner's penis.

Dr Kegel got his patients to practise these exercises two to three times a day for up to an hour at a time, but remember they suffered incontinence rather than just a need to jazz up their sex life. Kegel did suggest that around forty hours of training is all that is needed. Martica Heaner recommends seven minutes a day, while other sexperts suggest ten clenches on waking and another ten when you go to bed at night. The good thing about Kegels is that you can do them at any time of the day – standing up, lying down or walking – so try to fit them in where you can. In general, it takes about six to twelve weeks to see a real difference.

Regular 'love squeezes' tighten and tone the muscles – a sure-fire way to put the zip back into your love life!

Secrets of the long-term loved-up

'We tend to the marriage. You have to spend time away from the kids, stay up late and talk, go to the movies and do crossword puzzles together. My husband and I still have date nights and look forward to them all week.'
Michelle Pfeiffer

'You have to keep creating a marriage. We talk about everything, we grow and change together because nothing stays the same; you've got to continue evolving.'
Kelly Preston, married to John Travolta

'Let him know you're happy. I smile whenever I see him. He always knows how thrilled I am that he's there with me.'
Melanie Griffiths

'Sexiness wears thin after a while, and beauty fades. But to be married to a man who makes you laugh every day – ah now, there's a real treat.'
Joanne Woodward, married to Paul Newman for five decades

Quiz:
What's your love-style?

Learning your love-style can help your love life, but not so much as getting to know your partner's love-style. Knowing your own love-style helps you to realise when you're making unrealistic demands of your lover, while understanding theirs is invaluable when they're getting on your nerves.

A psychologist called John A. Lee interviewed hundreds of people and concluded there were a number of different ways of being in a relationship. Understanding this makes it a whole lot easier to keep your sex life on course. His book, *Lovestyles*, contains a definitive quiz to help you recognise your own and your partner's love-style but this shortened version could provide some clues. Select the style (or styles) that seem more like you and your mate. According to Lee's research, 75% of the people in each group manifest these characteristics. So where do you fit in? No one style is better than another although clearly the styles that don't resemble you at all might seem pretty damn weird!

Are you Eros?

- You see someone across a room and 'just know' they're for you.
- Sexual feelings are important – love is central to your life.
- It's hard for you to find the right one – you're choosy.

Are you Storge?

- Love will fade but you can live with a friend for life.
- For you, love is the basis of a strong community.
- When you're good friends with someone, sexual problems can be resolved.

Are you Ludus?

- You hate to be tied down to events in the future with a partner.
- In the past you have been accused of being emotionally immature or commitment-phobic.
- You find lots of different types attractive.

Are you Mania?

- For you being in love is synonymous with anxiety, even obsession.
- You're capable of losing weight, sleep and sometimes even your sanity when you're truly in love.
- It takes a long time for you to recover from a break-up – inevitably you're the dumped and not the dumper.

Are you Pragma?

- There's a shopping list of criteria that you expect your partner to fulfil.
- You believe you can master any goal with common sense – including a successful relationship.
- You'd never end up with someone who didn't fit in with your ambitions for your life and your social group.

Eros lovers have an idealised physical image of their lover but equally they believe they are on the planet to love one other person unstintingly – they've just got to find them! They stay loyal as long as romance is high on the agenda. If you're with an Erotic lover, don't forget romance.

Ludus lovers are often frustrated with aspects of their lives and unwilling to commit themselves in a love relationship. A pure 'Ludus' will be concerned about causing hurt and warn lovers in advance that commitment will be shaky, to put it mildly. Some are less scrupulous. Ludics avoid seeing their partner too often at the beginning of the relationship and even if they do marry, often there will be distance and secrets. Love is a banquet and they want to try it all. This drives Erotic and Manic partners mad while their attitude bores and even scares some Ludics.

Storge lovers often grow up in supportive families and communities. They expect their partners to be 'special' friends. Storgics do not become preoccupied with love but in a long-term relationship they get very possessive if their love (their status quo) is threatened and will fight tooth and nail to retain a lover. If the commitment isn't there, sexual interest palls. Love is not an end in itself; for them, it's part and parcel of life or it doesn't work.

Mania lovers are the potential stalkers in the pack. They expect love to be difficult and all-consuming – and for them it is because they are jealous and possessive. It's a rare person who wants a Mania love in the long term and so it's no surprise that they are almost inevitably abandoned.

Pragma lovers are the opposite. They won't fall in love with people who don't 'fit' in with their lives, plans and goals. Excessive emotion and jealous scenes are regarded with disdain, but they do appreciate signs of commitment. They'd like to have a love relationship but not if this means sacrificing peace of mind and their comfortable lifestyle. If it comes to it, they are most suited to living alone so beware if your partner is pragmatic – don't rock the boat too much!

Often one love-style predominates but a person can be a mixture of two or three. It's not worth getting hung up on this because such categorising can never be definitive. After all, we are human. It does, however, encourage more understanding of your partner's foibles. If you're with an Erotic, just accept they get horribly excited by visual images of people who fit into their ideal – which is why he's eyeing up that Italian waitress. Realising they are also the style who invest most in their romantic ideal of love may give you some reassurance, though. Similarly, if you're with a Ludus, understanding they are naturally restless may allow you more patience with them. It's not just you, everything in their life is vaguely dissatisfying. They can't help it; it's how they're made and you can't change that – only they can do so.

Lust up your mind

Simply think about it more, and you'll want it more! Counsellor Sarah Litvinoff states, 'Sex therapists often find that women who claim never to have been sexually interested or who have gone off sex, never think sexual thoughts. Many people narrowly define sexual fantasies as the mini-pornographic scenes you play out in your head, which might include, say, bondage or lesbian images that are a mental turn-on, but which you wouldn't necessarily enjoy enacting for real. But, in fact, any sexual thought is sexual fantasy.'

And any sort of sexual thought gets the job done.

Let your mind wander, look for the lascivious and feel the throb of sex that lies beneath the layers of our sophisticated lifestyle. Find stimulation in your daily routine and you'll overspill with erotic charge, which in turn will translate into action. You'll initiate sex and respond to your partner sexually in a different way.

Begin to make a habit of daydreaming about sex. First thing when you wake up in the morning or just before you go to sleep, think a dirty thought or two. When you're commuting, let the last time you made love run through your mind. As you're queuing or waiting for your train, relive your sexual greatest hits. Remember, every time sex flits across your mind it's a fantasy, and those who fantasise most have the best sex lives.

If you have a regular partner, you may feel a bit guilty about this. But this is all in your mind: it's harmless, it's cheap and what's more, it's private. Remember when you were a teenager and each time a remotely attractive stranger came across your radar, you began to imagine the possibilities and flirted, if at all possible? Think of fantasy in that way; harmless imaginings that won't go anywhere.

You could visualise slamming any attractive man you meet against the wall and kissing him wildly. On the surface you're shaking hands and mouthing platitudes. The man knows nothing of it, but the sexual frisson created by those images fuels your own idea of your sexual self. Your reasons for doing it have absolutely nothing to do with a desire for infidelity.

If you really struggle to come up with a sexual fantasy, start this way: imagine yourself being as sexually attractive as you can be. In your mind, you're drop-dead gorgeous. Move on to visualising this gorgeous you having sex. Stick with this for a while and see what happens.

Remember the words of Erica Jong: 'You are what you dream. You are what you daydream. Masters and Johnson's charts and numbers and flashing lights and plastic pricks tell us everything about sex and nothing about it. Because sex is all in the head.'

Like faith healing, you don't have to believe in this for it to work.

Any sort of sexual thought gets the job done

Keep him caring (how to keep your relationship minty-fresh)

Read, digest and ponder. Then get your diary, a big red pen and start to prioritise your relationship!

This chapter contains the three golden rules of a healthy relationship – the *sine qua non* of sexual happiness. All the technique and creativity in the world won't fix the sex in a relationship where the couple is together, but not together. On the other hand, couples who spend time together, and anticipate and plan for those moments, find it hard to lose interest in one another.

Rule 1: Daily

How is your partner feeling right now? What's happening at work? How are his relationships with friends, colleagues, siblings, parents? Carve out 15 minutes of each day to talk. If you find yourselves getting into a rut of busy-ness, when you pass like ships in the night for several days in a row without touching base, go to bed before your usual time or get up earlier and have a coffee together so you can touch base.

Kiss each other every morning before you get out of bed. Take the time for a swift cuddle. Breathe deeply, hold tight. Do the same at night. Never take your physical intimacy for granted. You found each other. That's pretty amazing and worth acknowledging with at least a daily hug.

Rule 2: Weekly

Where possible, go out with each other once a week. Once a fortnight is the bare minimum. According to the experts, this is the most important thing you can do. Couples who keep dating, keep mating. Spending too long sloping around the same house does something to a couple's sexual interest in each other and what it does generally isn't good. So get out, preferably after making some small effort to glam yourself up for your partner. Let them see why they bothered with you in the first place. And no, this isn't rocket science but it works!

Rule 3: Monthly

Go for a mini-adventure – shared memories cement your relationship. Make yours as mad or staid as you like, but at the least make sure it's something that you haven't done since the beginning of your relationship. It really doesn't matter what it is, so long as it's not your usual 'date'. What's the point? You see your partner coping with new environments and new skills and that keeps you interested in them. And them in you. Simple.

Research shows quite clearly that one of the defining differences between strong couples and those who drift is the amount of time and effort spent on shared pursuits. All of us have heard the advice, 'Spend more time with each other, being as interesting as possible.' But how many couples do you know who actually do this? I'm prepared to bet that those who do appear happiest.

Yes, but...

So you really, really don't think you can get out once a week? You don't have to go out for long – an hour or two is fine. Even parents of newborns will find a way, if sufficiently motivated.

No money? Make it a challenge to have a good night out on a small amount of cash. If all else fails, go for a walk and treat yourself to half a pint of lager at your local. Oh OK, share half a pint if money's really tight!

No childcare? Make it your mission to seek out other couples with kids who live locally – ideally, in the next street – and look like they enjoy going out (single parents and confirmed stay-at-homes are no good for this). The deal is that one half of their couple comes to your house and sits with your kids once a week. The next week one of you returns the favour. It means that for one night's babysitting you get two nights out and an evening home alone. Not bad!

Single parent? Swap your services so you can get time for fun.

No conversation? You'd better fix this one before you do anything else (see above).

Try something different

Stuck for inspiration when it comes to dating? Here's a year's worth of ideas!

- *Hill-walk between two cosy pubs*
- *Hire some cycles*
- *Dine al fresco – with champagne and strawberries*
- *Go horse riding*
- *Or paragliding*
- *Spend a weekend in a city you've never visited before*
- *Punt along a river or take out a rowing boat in your local park*
- *Watch a matinée at the cinema*
- *Spend the day at a health spa*
- *Visit an art gallery*
- *Go to the theatre*
- *Attend a self-help seminar*
- *Take turns to suggest the adventure, and go along with your partner's choice, even if you don't fancy it. Even the disasters will give you shared memories to laugh about afterwards.*

Q and A:
It's all *his* fault

Q. His oral sex technique has improved a lot since I met him, but it's still not hitting the right buttons. What now?

A. If your communication is good then you'll just have to show him. Make it during a very steamy session where you're both a bit crazed with passion and he wants to do anything to get you off. Ask him, 'Would you mind trying this? I've been thinking it would really drive me crazy.' Then show him with your own tongue, on his bicep, palm or any other flat surface (men can do this on a woman's finger or toes) – make sure he can see what your tongue is doing and how fast it's going. Back this up with instructions, but only a little at a time. Aim for a 10% improvement every time. And praise, praise, praise.

Q. I find my partner less attractive since he got fat. He keeps saying he'll do something about it, but his attempts last two days max. Am I being unreasonable?

A. Your attitude is just the sort that won't help. Research studies have shown that it takes people many attempts to succeed at reaching a weight goal, but if they persevere, they'll get there. One of the factors that helps them is the unwavering, non-judgemental support of family. That's you!

Q. My partner's interest is hours spent in internet chatrooms. What's gone wrong?

A. You're insecure in your relationship and probably with good reason. Whatever your partner chooses to do on his own that you view as a threat – chatrooms, lap dancing, drinking, Smurf collecting – isn't a problem in itself. It's the fact that you perceive it as a threat that's the problem. Yours is not a happy ship or your partner would stop or significantly cut down on the chatrooms when you express discomfort. It's time to start talking, perhaps with the help of a professional counsellor.

Q. My partner won't share anything. How can I change the situation?

A. When you're distant, a short-cut to getting on better is simply to act as if your relationship is perfect – if your lover never speaks to you, carry on talking to them as if they're the world's greatest listener; if your lover no longer shows affection spontaneously, carry on hugging. Sounds crazy, but the change from negative to positive somehow seeps through to your partner at least long enough for you to ask them to behave more lovingly and for them to hear what you're saying.

Keep asking to share, and suggest counselling – if he won't go with you, consider going on your own. If he refuses to go, you might decide just to put up with the situation and find some mates with the emotional depth you crave. Long-term, this could be hell on your sex life and only you can decide if this is what you want forever. Through counselling, you can explore this. You may find a strange thing happening: the more you concentrate on what you want from life without reference to him, the more he might be drawn to keep himself relevant to you.

Not in the mood?

If bungee jumping could do the same for
us as sex can, we'd all be queuing up to try it!
When you just don't fancy it, this should
remind you of why it's worth doing…

There are minor and major reasons for periods when we don't much fancy sex. If you're going through one of those times right now, it's really worth your while to discover what's going on. Answer yes or no to the following questions:

1. Do you enjoy sex when you get going and then think, 'We should do this more often'?
2. Are there any physical reasons why you avoid sex?
3. Are there any psychological reasons why sex is not on the agenda?
4. Would you simply rather read gardening catalogues or watch *Big Brother* than have sex?

If you answered yes to questions 2 and 3, then this idea won't help. You should seek professional help. If you answered yes to 1 and/or 4 then it's time for some tough love. You owe it to your body to have sex, you owe it to your psyche to have sex and almost certainly you owe it to your relationship.

In a long-term relationship, wanting sex is a 'mind thing' as much as a physical imperative. The next time you sense a resistance to the idea of sex, remember the words of Tom Hopkins, best-selling author of *How to Master the Art of*

Selling: 'Winners almost always do what they think is the most productive thing possible at every given moment: losers never do.' Sometimes the most productive use of your time is to watch the sunset or talk to your spouse. Often, the most productive use of your time is having sex. Done well, with passion and enthusiasm, half an hour's sex is worth hours of doing just about anything else; it's the ultimate multi-tasking activity. It's not just good for your relationship, it's great for you, too. When you're dithering about whether or not to go for it, remember all that sex can do for you. Then ask yourself, 'Am I a winner or a loser?'

Your mission: To overcome a 'take it or leave it' attitude to sex.

Your task: Read the following each day for the next week and thereafter once a week.

Sex defuses stress

'Progressive relaxation' is a relaxation technique that involves tensing and then relaxing muscles in a controlled manner throughout the body. After a while, it sends you to sleep. Orgasmic sex works in much the same way. It also involves tensing and relaxing your muscles, but far more intensely. The result is that people with fulfilling sex lives are generally far less stressed, suffer fewer anxieties and bizarrely, they are more likely to take responsibility for their own lives (one of the prime characteristics of a successful person, apparently).

Sex boosts self-esteem

Good sex makes us feel better about ourselves because it can be such an intimate experience. You're letting your soul out for a little play in front of another person, and it's a huge ego kick if they like what they see. Of course, if they don't seem to enjoy this or, even worse, are so self-absorbed they don't appear to notice that's what you're doing, then it might be best to avoid having sex with such personalities because it won't be good for your self-esteem.

Sex is therapeutic

The Chinese believe that you can treat everything from a cold to eczema with sex. One thing's for sure, metaphorically and literally, it's good for your heart. One study looked at the sex lives of women who had been admitted to hospital following a heart attack. Of these, 65% reported that they experienced no sexual feelings or were

Ask yourself,
'Am I a winner or a loser?'

unhappy with their sex lives in some way. When researchers asked women who were hospitalised for other, non heart-related conditions, only 24% reported having non-existent or poor-quality sex lives.

Sex is creative

In an ideal world we'd all be scribbling away in diaries or expressing our emotions through dance and no doubt we'd be a happier, less repressed society for it. But who would feed the cat?

Seriously, most of us don't make time to express our emotions or even to recognise them as they flit across our consciousness. During sex is a perfect time to get back in touch with your inner self. As you touch each other, imagine you're expressing how you feel right at that moment. How are you feeling? Angry, sad, happy, secure, frustrated? Communicate this to your lover through your touch, words and actions.

Sex helps you live longer

It's true. Studies have shown that individuals with a healthy sex life are more resistant to disease and the ill-effects of stress. An orgasm boosts the body's white cell count (the cells that fight infection) by up to 20%. But note that we're talking about a *happy* love life here. Most probably, joyless sex won't confer any benefits, although so far no one has done the studies. We don't know why good sex works, but it's probably partly to do with the beneficial effects of having someone stroke you lovingly. Your immune system improves when you're caressed, stroked and hugged.

In summary, feeling like sex is a fragile flower that rarely blooms. Just do it! There are all sorts of complex psychological reasons why we go off sex with a long-term partner. Allow this to happen and inertia sets in. Reverse that mindset by reading about the benefits of sex repeatedly. OK, it's a brainwashing thing.

If both you and your partner are totally happy with little or no sex, fine. But if there's any sort of discrepancy, work a little harder at getting yourself in the mood more often. Think about sex more, pleasure yourself, make your daily life as sensual as possible. If your partner doesn't deliver what you need to enjoy sex, then you must talk to him. Above all else, remember that 'use it or lose it' applies in spades when it comes to sex.

Find a scent or two that speaks to you of sensuality

Nurture your inner goddess

In the bustle of everyday life, have you overlooked one very important person – you? Rethink the basics below and you'll feel incredibly sexy.

What helps your sex life more than you can imagine is simply feeling more sensual, preferably all of the time. Don't dismiss what follows as self-evident. Just follow the suggestions and see if you don't feel more empowered, more sensual and more attractive.

Fragrance

Take a couple of hours to drift around your nearest department store, exploring the world of fragrance. Simply shut your eyes and sniff. Keep going until you find a scent or two that speaks to you of sensuality, passion, that makes you feel irresistible. Go on, treat yourself. Of course you already know the concept of signature scent – this is about looking for your sexual signature scent, the one you'll wear for sex. When you wear this fragrance during the day it will immediately transport you back to some happy memories – and make you smile. With anticipation.

Clothes

First, throw out anything that doesn't make you feel comfortable. Next, get rid of garments that don't make you look gorgeous. Your aim is to feel you look your best all of the time. If you haven't much left in your wardrobe, go shopping for clothes that make you feel marvellous, ooze confidence and walk tall. Hint: this is easiest in clothes that drape your body and feel sensual – silk, cashmere, velvet, chiffon, chenille. It also goes for your night clothes. Are they beautiful, flattering, sensuous? If not, why not?

Lingerie

A must. It's not enough to wear a sensible set that doesn't quite match. Get professionally measured to check your bra size is correct. If you've been getting it wrong, the right bra will take years (and inches) off you. Perfect underwear makes you feel that you can take on the world. Drab, even greying garments will subtly undermine you all day without you even realising it's happening. Why? Because it's a sign that you don't value yourself much in the sensuality states. So why should anyone else?

Treat yourself to whatever sort of lingerie makes you feel womanly and clever (yes, you read that right!). And buy enough so you can enjoy the boost that it gives you every day of the week.

Two

Communicate, connect… and it's not all about talking

Whatever helps you connect will help your love life – and that doesn't always mean talking.

Stop having sex

Are you bored with sex? Then take a break.
You may find out you connect more without
it. Focusing on sensuality rather than sex can
remind you why sex is worth bothering
with in the first place.

The top tool in the sexual counselling box of tricks is a technique called 'sensate focus'. To put it frankly, you make a pact not to have penetrative sex. When couples go to see a sex therapist, often they will be asked to refrain from making love until they've worked through their issues, one by one. Couples will frequently spend weeks simply holding each other, working up to touching each other non-sexually through techniques such as massage before finally moving on to sexual pleasuring without penetrative sex.

If you got stuck at the beginning of that last sentence, focusing on the word 'weeks' with dread, then relax. You won't have to give up sex for all that long to achieve astounding results. Abstaining from sex altogether may sound extreme: but taking a holiday from disappointed expectations and performance pressure and, instead, spending time getting to know each other again through strictly non-penetrative contact works wonders when it comes to regaining passion. Ripping apart old patterns of relating to each other gets couples back to basics. Simply spending time together, trying to make your partner feel good is powerful. You'll remember what all the fuss was about in the first place.

Expert Tracey Cox says sex is like chocolate – if we get too much of a good thing, we go off it. Think how much better chocolate tastes after you've given it up for Lent. It's the same with sex. Too much and we become jaded and take it for granted. You might be far from needing sex therapy, but there are few couples who wouldn't benefit from a spot of sensate focus to encourage better communication and spark libido, so choose a week when you both decide that you won't have penetrative sex.

Day 1: On the first night you cuddle up together on the couch.

Day 2: Go to bed an hour early. Naked. Lie in bed stroking and touching each other. Talk about your lives. Reconnect.

Day 3: Take a shower or bath together with sensual oils.

Day 4: She gives him a long, all-over massage.

Day 5: He gives her a long, all-over massage.

Day 6: She massages him, including touching him sexually but not to the point where he has an orgasm. She can explore his reactions to various kinds of touching and ask for feedback.

Day 7: He does the same for her.

Day 8: By now the sexual tension between you should be causing visible sparks!

If you don't have a clear week to devote to this project, try some speed sensate focus. It's like speed dating, only less embarrassing! Use sensory deprivation to help you focus on the power of touch. It's a brilliant reminder that when we're tired and wired, our bodies can give us supreme physical pleasure. The more senses cut off, the more we appreciate the ones that remain. Blindfold your partner and then insist they relax totally for the next 15 minutes. They could wear earplugs, too, to really sink into their own world of sensory delight. Play some soft music and light a few candles. Ask your partner to lie back on comfortable pillows or a duvet. They should be naked and you should either be lightly dressed or naked. The room should be warm!

Using a long feather or a soft silk scarf, stroke every part of your partner's body, not just the usual erogenous zones.

Feel good now: *If you're having problems finding your G-spot, feel for it after you've had an orgasm. The urethral sponge will have swelled, making it easier to locate.*

Keep the touch gentle and continuous. Finally, blow gently over their skin everywhere the feather or silk touched. You can then swap over.

Remember: the need to be held lovingly is fundamental to our being. Scientists believe it could be as important in human behavioural development as food and water. We crave sensual touch and for many of us sex is the means whereby we obtain it. Orgasm could simply be the pay-off that nature has built into our physiological make-up to ensure we seek out physical closeness, especially where women are concerned since orgasm isn't strictly necessary for reproduction.

Sex is like chocolate –
if we get too much
we go off it

Ask for what you want

So, how do you get your lover to love you the way you want to be loved? Just because you've been together forever doesn't mean you press each other's buttons absolutely perfectly.

Yet the man or woman who can tell their lover that they want to be touched differently from the way they've been touched a million times before is pretty rare.

But you can ask without embarrassing yourself and mortifying your lover in the process. Here's how to persuade them to do something differently when they think they've been getting it right for years. Always find something positive to say, but don't praise what's bad. Remember, pretending to enjoy what you don't is where you went wrong in the first place.

The wrong way

Using phrases that start with 'Why don't you…', 'You never…' or 'That doesn't…' just cause offence and your partner will get defensive. Moreover, whining about the problem is deeply unattractive too.

The right way

Step 1: Praise, praise, praise – your new resolution
From now on, be an appreciative lover. Every chance you get, praise your partner's performance and use every way you can think of to do this. This will create a win–win situation. Be especially appreciative during sex. Do it with body language, do it loudly, spell it out: 'I love everything you do in bed', 'You're just so sexy', 'No one's ever done that to me the way that you do'. They should finish each lovemaking session assured that you're blissfully happy.

If you're not an expressive lover, make this your modus operandi from now on. For one thing, this technique will backfire spectacularly on you if you stop as soon as you get what you want – it will look like a cynical ploy (it will be). There's nothing to be ashamed of in building up confidence in your lover. Their win is that you create an atmosphere where they can't fail; they won't fear trying something new if they sense your happiness doesn't depend on it. If they get it wrong or if they don't want to go through with it, they've nothing to lose because they know just how much you value them. Your win is that besides being a lovely person, you're also gearing them up for moving your sex life on to greater heights.

Step 2: Focus on the positive

Once you've created a climate of confidence, you can modify your partner's technique by focusing on the positive. For instance, 'I love the way you do that, especially when you go slowly/quickly/hang off the bedside table while you're doing it'. The other great bonus of this approach is that within reason it doesn't matter if it's a complete lie. For example, your lover may go down on you with the subtlety of a rotodriver, but if you tell him how lovely it is when his mouth goes really slowly then he'll probably believe you. He'll almost certainly start doing it more slowly too. For you, the payoff is that you'll get more of what you want.

Use discretion and be specific, where possible. And you really need to use your hands to gently direct the action the way you want it.

Step 3: Suggest how they might change

Now you can suggest doing things differently but do this with grace. It must also be said lightly, not as if your entire sexual happiness depends on it (remember, they mustn't fail!). Say that you've read about something you'd like to try in a book and ask if they would oblige…

Praise your partner's performance

Feel good now: *Look for easy ways to cheer your partner up. Pick up a tub of her favourite ice cream on the way home from work. Run him a bath and bring him a cold beer. Sappy gestures work and needn't be expensive – they build up a huge bank of goodwill that couples can draw on when life gets stressful.*

What's your LQ?

Often we know more about what lights
the candle of the person sitting next to
us at work than the one we've chosen
to share our lives with.

John Gray, author of the best-selling *Men are from Mars, Women are from Venus*, made a good point, directed at men: if your partner adores chocolates and sees them as the eternal proof that you love her, why on earth would you buy her roses? Yet the world is full of guys who show up with bunches of roses and wonder why they get them thrown at their heads. The moral is simple: if your lover needs chocolates to make them feel loved, give 'em chocolates! Whether you think a bunch of red roses is more romantic is irrelevant. Broadly speaking, to successfully love the one we're with, we need to understand what they need to feel loved. To keep their love, we must give them what they need at least as far as possible. Lots of couples have indifferent or absolutely no sex, not because they don't spark off each other but because for years they haven't felt loved by their partner.

When your lover feels insecure, stressed or worried, how do you make them feel safe and reassured? Does it work? If not, do you know what does? What makes it easier to get closer? Would your partner prefer a romantic meal or a wild night out on the town as the prelude to sex? Do you occasionally indulge them, even if you'd rather do something else?

Does your partner feel closer to you when you're laughing together or being upset with you? If the answer's 'upset', do you respond in a way that seems to satisfy them or are they disappointed in you? If laughing is your thing, when was the last time you went out of your way to make sure you had a good laugh together? What's your lover's favourite way of resolving a fight (not necessarily the way you always resolve it)?

These are the kind of questions that you have to know the answers to. And your partner, of course, needs to know what works for you. Emotionally, we have to be given chocolates at least some of the time or we start to shut off from our partner and get tempted by someone who appears to offer Milk Tray on demand. If you're with a person for whom chocolate equals love, all the roses in the world won't fix your relationship or help you get good sex.

Give 'em chocolates!

Tantric sex

No, it's just a load of old joss sticks!
Tantric sex really can help you reconnect.
If you've absolutely had it with your partner's
idea of foreplay being a quick tap on
your shoulder and a hopeful expression,
it's time to go Tantric.

To the student of Tantra, sex is sacred, a means of accessing spirituality and a way to meditate, transcend problems and ultimately reach a more blissful state. For those of us who don't have the time or inclination to study Tantric sex in any great depth, a little knowledge can still add a lot to our love lives. Tantra teaches sex is important and by clearing time to undergo a few of the simpler rituals you declare to each other, 'Hey, our sex life is a priority'.

Tantric sex teaches you to concentrate on your lover and on the sensations that you're experiencing. Forget the orgasm! What's important is the journey, not the arrival. And for that reason alone, Tantra can be a liberating and mind-altering experience, even if you don't get into it the whole way.

Ritual one: create a temple of love

A really simple method of foreplay is to transform your bedroom into a sensual haven that's quite different to the rest of your home. You don't have to opt for lurid leopard prints and black walls – unless that's your preferred style, of course. Take a long look at your bedroom as if you are seeing it for the first time. Does your interior say 'love', 'passion', 'excitement'? Is it a room devoted to the two of you?

First, think about what's in the room. Would you say that the TV contributes to improving your love life? Unless you use it mainly to watch porn, probably not. Perhaps you spend more time watching it than talking to each other. If you want to keep the TV, find a scarf to cover it as a mental signal that you're switching off from the outside world. Similarly, ban work paraphernalia and also piles of clothes waiting to be ironed, family photos, anything that takes your attention away from each other and onto your responsibilities. Repair and clean tatty or old furnishings. Clear away clutter. Throw open the windows and let fresh air circulate. This room is a reflection of your relationship – it's where you spend the most time with each other; it should sparkle.

Finally, create a love altar. Find a picture of the two of you together that symbolises the best in your relationship. Whenever you look at it, you should feel warm and compassionate towards your partner and strong as a couple. Place it in a nice frame where you can see it easily every day. Keep fresh flowers beside it and candles – anything that you have to tend to regularly and pay attention to – as a physical reminder that your relationship needs tending, too.

None of this is genius level, but think of your own and your friends' bedrooms. How many have been designed with sensuality, luxury, comfort and sex in mind? Your bedroom should be a place that's welcoming to both of you, so that you find yourself looking forward to hanging out in the only place where most couples can be truly intimate and private with each other.

Ritual two: think yourself in love

Tantric sex depends on visualisation to build sexual energy. As your lover begins to caress you, feel how much they love you. Imagine their love for you flowing from their fingertips and hands, nurturing you.

Melt into their embrace. When they kiss you, feel that with each kiss they are showing you how much they love you. Imagine the sexual energy that you are creating between you is visible as a red or pink light emanating from your genitals and surrounding you like a force field of love. As your partner touches you, imagine your arousal growing like a great wave of light. See it as fire or energy that emerges from your deep pelvis and adds to the force field surrounding and supporting you. As you begin to have sex, imagine the energy passing upwards from the base of your spine to your heart; feel this energy as love around your heart, feel it as joy. Imagine it reaching out and surrounding your partner's heart. Then, as you get more excited, imagine the energy being drawn upwards and flowing out through the top of your head.

That's the way to enlightenment, but it takes practice. Look on the bright side, with all that visualising going on at least you won't be thinking about who's doing the school run tomorrow!

Tantric sex is a discipline – with practice, feelings grow. If you believe in the basic concept that sex is a way to deepen and enrich your life, then invest in a good book about Tantric sex. With practice, couples can keep going for hours – if that's what they want. But even Sting, the most famous proponent of Tantric sex, cracked the joke that when he'd gone public about his seven-hour sex sessions, he hadn't mentioned that five and a half hours were taken up with dinner and a movie! Don't get too attached to the outcome.

Create a temple of love

Overcoming exhaustion

Couples frazzled by the sheer weight of the goals they set themselves often compete as to how tired they are. You've worked for it and by God, you've got it – a life so totally, overwhelmingly busy that you simply don't have the energy for sex!

Of course, it's not the end of a relationship if you go for some time with a lacklustre, or indeed non-existent love life. Every relationship has its down-time. But the major worry with the tiredness reason for avoiding sex is that it gains a weird sort of reverse momentum. Keep using tiredness as an excuse and before you know it, inertia sets in. What you need is a two-pronged attack.

If lovemaking usually takes place just before bed and is generally rushed and unsatisfying because you're both knackered, make a weekly tryst for sex, where you go to bed early and enjoy each other. Therapists agree that this 'appointment system' is one of the easiest ways to ease you back into a good sex life.

First prong: get over yourself

Here's a fact: having sex when you're tired is not against the Geneva Convention. Lovemaking can start off indifferently and get a whole lot better. And even if it doesn't, in a longstanding relationship, indifferent sex is better than no sex. At least you've got something to work on.

If you're of the aficionado brigade who, unless sex is a multi-orgasmic garden of delight, would rather not bother then you have to negotiate this with your partner. Make definite dates when you're going to do it: sex that day is your priority. See it as a red-letter event.

Second prong: reorganise your workload
If you're in a couple with young children and having no sex, usually a resentment on the part of one partner towards the other lies at the root of this. Often the woman is resentful of the man. Usually she is working, even if only part time, and she may be doing most of the childcare too. Frequently, women who have given up work to look after their kids also feel that what they do isn't appreciated.

So, who does the most after a hard day's work?
This quiz gives couples a quick visual reference as to who does more around the home. It assumes you're both working. Tick the sex of the partner who most often undertakes a particular task. This test can be an eye-opener for couples who think they have a pretty equal relationship.

If it's not so balanced, take steps to delegate or equalise your workload – or your sex life is unlikely to get back to normal any time soon!

Getting the children ready for the day	M/F
Making breakfast	M/F
Preparing packed lunches	M/F
Doing the school run	M/F
Supervising homework	M/F
Teachers' meetings	M/F
Immunisations, trips to the GP	M/F
Dealing with childcare generally	M/F
Bathing children and getting them ready for bed	M/F
Bedtime stories	M/F
Arranging play dates with other parents	M/F
Supermarket shopping	M/F
Cooking dinner	M/F
Clearing the house at the end of the evening	M/F
Paying bills	M/F
DIY, organising repairs	M/F
Cleaning	M/F
Taking out the trash	M/F
Buying children's clothes	M/F
Washing and drying clothes	M/F
Dishwasher loading	M/F

Gardening	M/F
Maintaining and cleaning the car	M/F
Organising your social life/holidays	M/F

You might be reading this and thinking, 'I'm the major breadwinner, I work my backside off and I can't do childcare too.' But for the sake of your relationship, you'll have to find some compromise. Talk openly about how you divide your joint workload, give each other the space to have a life as an individual and find time to spend as a couple. If you're reading this and thinking, 'Who needs a quiz to tell me I do it all?' then stop and examine your martyr-syndrome. And yes, that's you. Get rid of it at all costs or 'I'm just so tired' will sound the death knell for your sex life and possibly over time your relationship too.

Overprotective parents take note: someone else can very well look after your children. Your relationship with one another, however, cannot be tended by anyone else but the two of you. Workaholics also take note: pop your clogs tomorrow and someone else will fill your role by Monday morning. No one else can quite take your place in your relationship.

Make definite dates when you're going to do it

Sharing secrets

Point your lover in the right direction by asserting your sexual identity. Express yourself to lovers, in your diary or under a nom de plume on the net.

Psychologists advise that communication in any relationship is important, but there are many ways to make your desires known. Talking is easy when things are going right; the problems start when they get jaded, or go downhill. Often couples walk an emotional minefield during such a time, each afraid to let on to the other that something is amiss. Talking about the big 'O' is particularly difficult because many people are afraid of hurting their partner's feelings.

In *Sex Talk*, sex therapist Aline P. Zoldbrod says that one of the best ways to communicate about sex is to build on your positive experiences: 'Flip through your memories and zero in on one time that really blew the others out of the water.'

Feel good now: *Getting in the mood for sex? Try being 'on call' like a porn star and wait in a carefully appointed dressing room: have your partner pop his head round the door every now and then to bring you drinks. You'll feel fresh and look gorgeous, and perhaps waiting for your partner to tell you that 'they' are ready for you will even heighten your anticipation.*

Once you work out the red-hot bits that turn you both on, use these more often in your sexual repertoire.

To get you in the mood for talking frankly, you could watch a film about sex (erotic or otherwise) to make the subject easier to discuss. If you can't bring yourself to watch anything erotic yet, talk about the married couple in *American Beauty* or any film that features modern relationships. You might also set aside a corner of your home as a den, where you can snuggle and talk to each other. Alternatively, signal a special time – Sunday brunch, perhaps – for sexy conversation.

Zoldbrod suggests going to a bookstore and studying the sex books together (a turn-on, at least!). Another tip from her is to draw a 'body' map signifying which areas you definitely like to be touched, which ones not, and those you are unsure about. If you don't feel you can sit and discuss this 'cold', then ask to be blindfolded and simply cry out in pleasure to illustrate; use ice or a tongue dipped in hot tea to help get the message across – the skin is the biggest erogenous zone and temperature differences accentuate pleasure.

Ask him to tell you a fantasy story; it can be anything. But once you've established this, ask him to tell you about his first sexual experience or even the first time he had sex with you. Work up to him confessing his 'fantasy' story with all the bits he never normally reveals.

To get over the risk of sharing personal histories, Zoldbrod suggests telling 'two hypotheticals and one truth' with your partner having to guess which one is true. You can choose to reveal the final truth when it feels comfortable.

There's also emails, texting, phone calls and journals. Some people find it easier to talk dirty over a phone because they can let their guard down without having to reveal their body language. Another tip is to write down your ideal fantasy and leave it somewhere your lover can read it. Make it sizzling hot, just how you'd like it to happen.

Ask to be blindfolded and simply cry out in pleasure to illustrate where you like to be touched

Dirty talk

Say it out loud, say it proud! The right
combination of pure filth whispered into your
lover's ear at the right moment can catapult him
into a thundering orgasm. Get it wrong, and
he'll be running for the door, though.

Done right, a few lewd and lascivious words are the simplest way of making your sex life sing – no props or cost involved. As writer Brigid McConville points out in her book, *Our Secret Lives*, in our culture there's a big taboo about talking about sex. Couples who start off filthy, don't stay that way. She says, 'The Big Ban on sex talk can start almost immediately in a relationship, intensifying to solid silence as the years go by. And by the time you've clocked up ten, twenty or more years, it's a hard habit to break.' Quite. So take it gently.

Talk dirty with conviction. To do this, commit to your talk. Talking dirty comes easily when you're in the first few stages of lust, purely because it's easiest with a virtual stranger. But when you've shared countless school meetings or fights over the remote, it's a whole lot harder. The other side of this is that you must try extra hard to support your lover's efforts. Don't undermine them with inopportune sniggering.

Four ways to add value to your verbal

1. Give feedback

The most basic form of dirty talk is to describe what's happening to you and what it feels like. For example, 'I love it when you kiss my collar bone like that.' A running commentary on what you're feeling and appreciating also serves to keep you 'in the moment', making it less likely that you'll start wondering who's going to get that promotion at work or if you have enough milk for breakfast. So encourage, praise, comment.

2. Build anticipation, make them beg

Tell your lover what you're going to do to them just before you do it. Ask if they like it; ask if they don't. Have them ask nicely for what they want; ask them to ask *not* so nicely. You get the idea. Before you know it, they're talking dirty, too. However, use this tactic with discretion. Endless questioning can swiftly move from sublime to downright annoying, risking the passion-melting retort 'Will you get on with it!').

3. Role-play makes it easier – a lot easier – to talk dirty

Think how much easier it could be if you were pretending to be someone else...

4. Read bedtime stories to each other

Sometimes it's not inhibition that gets in the way, it's lack of inspiration. After another hard day at the coalface of contemporary twenty-first-century life, making up a dirty scenario is just too much like hard work. That's when it pays to have a porn magazine kicking about under the bed. Women are often turned on by stories geared towards men and soft porn will supply most couples with some inspiration for reading aloud.

But if that's too 'right-off' for you, *Forum* magazine and the *Erotic Review* are aimed at both sexes and available at a newsagent near you. Or try reading a chapter a night from a Black Lace novel, a series aimed at exciting women but will also do the job for men. Another classic for reading to each other is *My Secret Garden*, a collection of women's sexual fantasies by Nancy Friday.

Final word

No one can give you a script for talking dirty. Transcribed, it always sounds ridiculous. You need to develop your own style together. The main thing is to just do it. Once you start saying dirty words out loud – even if they're someone else's dirty words – you'll soon find your groove.

Read bedtime stories to each other

Develop sexual mystique

Yes, it's possible. Even if you've shared
a bathroom for years.

If you want to keep your love life hot, difference is an Essential Thing. To carry on fancying your partner and to have him carry on fancying you, create a little distance between you, a little mystery, a little wildness in your soul. And if that doesn't come naturally, you need to work at it. In a nutshell, make it a habit that one night a week you do your own thing, no matter how busy you are. Remember, spending too much time inside together is terrible for your love life.

'Male and female are different,' says relationship counsellor Paula Hall. 'And we've known since the sixties that if a couple want a stable relationship, it's worth working at maintaining that difference. It's what keeps the electric buzz between them.' She points out that studies by psychologists have already picked up on the dangers of becoming too alike. 'We call it "enmeshment" when couples become too similar,' says Hall. 'It's been known for a long time that it can have a detrimental impact on sexual desire.'

You probably think it's cosy that you share the same interests, friends, hopes, dreams and taste in soft furnishings. So it is. Congratulations, you're terrific mates. Carry on regardless if you want a great relationship without particularly exciting, or indeed plentiful, sex. However, if you want sex that makes your toes curl, you need a little separateness to keep desire alive.

You can be all things to a partner, but not to a lover. Similarly, they cannot be all things to you. Marcel Proust said it best: 'An absence, the declining of an invitation to dinner, an unintentional, unconscious harshness are of more service than all the cosmetics and fine clothes in the world.'

There's an art to this. Every three or four months or so, you could be just a little bit cool with your partner. Nothing serious. Just switch off from him a bit, seem a little less easily pleased, a bit more interested in talking to friends on the phone. Lock yourself in the bathroom, submerge yourself in a book. This may sound trivial but it works like a charm.

Perhaps all this withdrawing interest sounds suspiciously like game-playing – and you know what? It is! You can fake it a little bit, but it doesn't always work. What does is if both partners do it for real – keep interested in life, stay full of vim and brio for other projects, remain engaged with people outside their relationship and be passionate about the world. Then, and here is the important bit, they bring that energy home and translate it into passion for each other. They do that by talking about their lives with such enthusiasm that their partners can't help getting a kick out of their enthusiasm, charm, intelligence and all-round top-quality personality.

Relationship psychologist Susan Quilliam points out that there are some straightforward ways of making sure your relationship doesn't sink into the mire of 'enmeshment':

Rule 1. All couples fall into a pattern of doing the same thing and being scared to suggest anything new because 'we don't do that'. But if you fancy doing something different, suggest it anyway. Don't argue if they say 'no'. The point has been made. You've reinforced in both your minds that you're individuals.

Rule 2. Support your partner as much as possible when they're trying to be an individual. Don't dismiss new ideas and interests without thinking them through carefully.

Rule 3. Be yourself. Don't take on his or her interests and hobbies unless they genuinely interest you, too. We're equal, but we're not the same.

So, what if you try to be distant, but your partner doesn't appear to notice? In some relationships, so the French say, there's always one offering a cheek to be kissed, and another doing the kissing. Being distant is tough for kissers because they're genuinely focused on their mates pretty much to the detriment of everything else and it's hard to fake indifference. He knows what you're trying to do and kind of likes it. And he'll ignore you even more.

In fact, that's the nature of the push–pull, passive–aggressive relationship you've formed. Until recently it's worked for you, but maybe now you want something different? The solution for you is the same as for anyone wanting to change a relationship: stop thinking about his reactions, expect nothing different from him and concentrate on you. You've gone beyond the stage of playing games. Reintroduce passion into your own life. It's time to get real. If he's the only thing that really gets your juices going, change that fast!

Spending too much time inside together is terrible for your love life

Three
Just like the first time

Want to get the thrill back?
Here are some ideas that work.

Make it a quick one

Done right, a quickie can deliver the sort of
thrills you may not have experienced since
adolescence. In fact, many couples applaud
the quickie – it fits nicely into their schedules.
But it isn't really a 'quickie' if it happens in bed;
that's just a snatched shag. For the same
amount of time or effort you could take
your sex life to another level.

Surreptitiousness, not speed, is the essence of the quickie. The reason why it needs to be fast is not that you're supposed to be doing something else instead, like making Sunday lunch for the in-laws, but that your mother-in-law could pop her head round the kitchen door at any moment and offer to help with the gravy. Until you've experienced a quickie where there's every chance you might get caught in the flagrant act, you haven't really had one at all.

Perhaps you doubt the aphrodisiac qualities of being caught? Think of all the couples you know who have maintained illicit 'relationships' for years, convinced they're in the grip of a great passion. The truth is they wouldn't last five minutes if their sex life wasn't almost entirely sneaky and speedy. Quickies make for addictive sex.

Now some people don't like quickies. They really don't. Your partner might have gone along with it when you first got together because frankly they'd have had sex suspended from Big Ben if you seemed to think it was a good idea. Maybe it's not really them and they don't feel comfortable if they think they'll get caught; they (usually men) can't bear the thought of being embarrassed, or they don't like getting messed up (usually women). And they don't even get an orgasm out of it (almost certainly this applies to women). So if your lover's in this category, you may have to accept 'no' gracefully or keep on trying but be prepared for a lot of rejection. Alternatively, you could just get very good at persuading your partner that fast, hot sex up against a wall is the best idea they never had.

Imagine…

Any minute now you're expecting guests to arrive. You're checking the barbie's hot enough or maybe that you've got enough gin when you catch sight of your partner as they pass by, looking gorgeous. You reach for them, throw them up against a wall, ravish them with kisses; your hands roam over and under clothes. Your lover is surprised but begins to kiss you back.

You glance at your watch. Your guests are expected to arrive in precisely 5 minutes. There's no time to undress. At any moment you might hear a ring on the doorbell. You fumble, push underwear aside, undo zips and buttons, reveal skin, pull clothes up and down so you achieve penetration. Fast and frantic sex is the only kind you've got time for. By the time your guests arrive only a slight breathlessness gives away your secret.

Any props needed?

None. Except if you're a woman with a predilection for quickies it helps if you choose easily accessible knickers. There's something delicious about pushing aside the fabric and it adds to the erotic charge. Thongs are good but your partner can end up with friction burns. French knickers? Oh yes!

So what's a good position?

Standing up is the traditional knee trembler but it's not terrific for any woman weighing more than 50.8 kg (112 lb). It's even worse for her man! However, you don't have to go for the full Monty. Instead of him taking the whole weight of your body, the woman can use a chair or table to support one leg. Or better still, he enters her from behind with her bent over slightly, so he has a good view of his penis entering.

Quickies make for addictive sex

Paying for it

You know, slutty sex may be a turn-on for both of you. Frequently, both sexes get a huge kick out of acting out prostitution fantasies. They explore our attitude to power and control (often erotically charged) and we're able to relish the freedom of imagining that we're having no-holds-barred, no-strings-attached sex.

The 'client' gets the thrill of the clean transaction, of the freedom of asking for what he wants, of control, of being in charge. The 'whore' obtains visible proof that he values what she does in bed. For the sake of clarity, we're coming over all traditional here and assuming 'he' is the client and 'she' the whore, but of course this fantasy begs for role reversal. The powerful female client and the stud-for-hire can be just as much of a turn-on.

This is one that definitely works better if you've both had a couple of drinks beforehand because alcohol removes any self-consciousness from role-playing and for this idea to really work, you both need to stay in character throughout.

1. The Classic

Arrange to meet on a certain street corner at a certain time. Make sure there's not the slightest chance of it being mistaken for a red-light area or you might get more reality than you bargained for. She should dress as overtly sexily as she feels comfortable with in public; simply slipping off her knickers beforehand gives that added frisson. At the appointed hour, he pulls up in his car and asks whether she is available. She replies, 'For what?' Then he tells her in explicit detail. She comes back with the cost. Haggling or 'negotiating a price' can be a turn-on and she shouldn't get in the car until the deal is done. You can now either drive back home and pretend it's her place or, if you're daring, use the car (somewhere private, of course, or again this game could get a bit too real).

2. The Pick-up

She's sitting at a hotel bar, looking sexy but demure. It helps if she adopts a slightly different look from usual – more make-up, hair slightly different, heels higher – a style that makes her feel unlike herself. She should make sure her underwear is brand new – nothing he's ever seen before. Similarly, she should order a different drink from usual and adopt a different name and personality – the easier the new persona comes to her, the more convincing this will be. The same applies to him: he should invent a new persona too and 'work it up'.

He approaches her and, although there may be some preliminary 'soft soap', eventually a conversation not unlike the one above has to take place. Maintain eye contact; it's sexier. When you're done, head home (or better still, take a room). Don't talk overly much.

3. The Hotel Room

Book a hotel room in advance. She arrives first and changes – a wig if she can bear it, lingerie he's never seen before, heels, different perfume, a negligée if she feels uncomfortable strutting around near-naked. Make the mood seductive with music and candles. She should psyche herself up – she's a high-class call girl and her job is to make him feel good. These girls are paid a lot because they're brilliant actresses so she should put her heart into it.

At last, he knocks on the door and she lets him in. Introduce yourselves by different names. Open a bottle of champagne. He can be nervous – that's still in character – but she must be confident and tease, flirt or be sexually voracious. She should read her client and take her clues from him (he, of course, has to act out his other side – the side that might frequent prostitutes). She must make it clear that she's there for one reason only – to give him the best sexual experience he's ever had. What would it take? What does he like? She should name her price and make it high. She's the ultimate indulgence; she's expensive.

When the price has been agreed and she has the cash, lead him to the bed and get down to business. She should remember that this is her job and she's very, very good at it. If she can slip a few tricks in that he definitely won't be expecting, all the better.

Finally, but very important: she gets to keep the money.

Porn-star secrets

So, what can the professionals teach us?

Best way to get in the mood?
'Often we don't take time to enjoy our bodies and to think of ourselves as sexual beings. Take a nice long languorous bath every day, really take time to wash and feel your body and think of yourself as sexy and beautiful.' Sharon Mitchell

'You might not really feel like having sex so much and then you take a shower and shave your legs and you're more open to the idea. Spending time on your hair and make-up makes you look hot and that makes you feel hot.' Stormy Daniels

Best position?
'In the standing missionary, the guy is standing up off the bed and I'm missionary, this enables me to reach down and play with myself so I can have an orgasm. He can see me completely and I can see him.' Taylor Wayne

Best technique?

'Anything as long as you don't do just one thing. You've got two hands and a mouth, use everything you can to stimulate all the different parts of the body. It all feels good and it will help to make the experience feel better for the other person.' Taylor Wayne

Best tip?

'After a hard day's work it's your legs that ache. It's all in the thighs, bum, glutes and quads. To get myself fit for sex, I do squats. From standing, just squat down like you're going to sit down and if you keep your arms above your head or rest your hands on your shoulders, it works every single muscle in the body, including the face.' Daisy Rock

Maintain eye contact; it's sexier

Coming over all touchy-feely

Learn to express sensuality with your whole body. Think of ways in which you can actively be more aware of your body during sex. Here are some ideas to get you started.

Step 1

Showering together is one of those things you do at the beginning of a relationship that tails off as the mortgage gets bigger. Give your lover a surprise this week. Wait until it's good and steamy in there, then strip off, step in and start soaping him down.

The noise of the shower cuts you off from the outside world, makes talk less likely and forces you to get physical together. But only, of course, if your shower is a powerful one. A pathetic dribble where you both edge the other one out to get a share of the water won't cut it! Put on some gorgeous wispy underwear and step into the shower with him when he's not expecting it. Naked's good, naked's great, but the feel (and look!) of wet fabric plastered against your slick body and the rush he'll get from pushing it aside to get at you should make for a different kind of experience.

Step 2

Look for different ways to surprise each other with unexpected sensations:

Wear something different from the norm. If you sleep naked, try silk pyjama bottoms. Do you always wear a nightdress? Change to a simple white cotton brief-and-vest set.

Introduce a feather into lovemaking. Ask your lover to close their eyes and trail it over their bare skin. Some people hate it, others love it, but it sensitises bare skin and makes it more reactive to other stimulation.

While your lover is bathing, heat up a towel with a hairdryer and offer it to them as they come out. A toasty hot towel is delicious, unexpected and will get you brownie points for thoughtfulness. Make sure they do the same for you.

Take an ice cube and rub it over your lover's bare back or nipples while you're making love until it melts. Take in the sensations, from shock through enjoyment. Couple with some gentle slaps if you want to get kinky. Heat, then cold is very sensitising.

Step 3

Marilyn Monroe's sexual signature note had nothing to do with her looks (her partner couldn't see her) or his degree of sexual satisfaction (he didn't even come) and everything to do with the electrifying power that touch can have on the average male, deprived as he might be of all-over, deeply sensual touch.

Marilyn, so the story goes, would ask her lover to lie on his front and remain very, very still. Once he was in position she'd straddle him from behind and whisper in his ear that he was going to help her to come. Then she'd liberally apply oil on his back and her body, and start slithering up and down on him, rubbing her vulva and clitoris against his back and buttocks, over and over again, finding just the right spot to grind her hips to give her the right pressure, whispering all the time how turned on she was, how hot she was, how close she was… until, finally, inevitably, she came. He probably quite enjoyed it too.

Clever Marilyn! What's more likely to make your lover mad for you than letting them know they drive you mad with lust, while ensuring they get to have a nice little lie-down at the same time?

Give your lover a surprise this week

Something for the weekend

Time spent away together intensifies your experiences. Making sex the focus of your break will revitalise your love life.

Bridget Jones turned the romantic 'mini-break' into a joke, but if your relationship has been in a bit of a slump, a few days away from it all really is a perfect opportunity to recharge your sexual batteries.

Prioritising sex rather than, say, sightseeing or gastro-pubbing will fire up your love life, possibly for months afterwards. The reason is that a new place lets you reinvent yourselves. You'll be more daring and more focused on each other. And if you have any problem areas, you can plan to sort them out over the weekend.

Here are some ideas for solving two common relationship problems during a typical two-day break. Use them as a model to build your own plans.

Problem: you're turning into friends rather than lovers

It's oh-so-very easy to get into the rut of being good companions rather than red-hot lovers. Everything about your break should be geared to remind you of the sensual things in life. Don't make it about catching up on culture, unless you happen to get fantastically turned on by modern art.

Think long, boozy lunches in shady cafés and then back to the hotel bed for a siesta because it's too damn hot to do much else. Think Spain or Italy. The sexual focus of the weekend should be on rediscovering your excitement in each other and forging the bond between you as lovers.

Day 1

Build excitement. Kiss, touch each other up, grope, spend hours on foreplay... but break out of your rut by not having sex. Pretend you are new lovers who aren't ready to move on to the sexual stage of a relationship. Be a little shy – shut the bathroom door. Take time with your appearance; see each other as you did in your first days together. Work

Feel good now: *Want to enjoy more powerful orgasms? Imagine your vagina has a lift inside it and you're going to elevate that lift using your PC muscles. Take the lift to the first floor, pause, second floor, pause, third floor, pause, top floor and pause. Now let the lift down again. Practise this, going as fast and then as slowly as possible.*

on feelings of compassion and affection for your lover –
view them through the same rose-coloured specs as you
did in the beginning. Be determined to find them deeply
endearing, no matter how much they were irritating you
yesterday; allow yourself to be charmed.

Day 2

Resolve to do something you'll never forget. Most probably,
you can remember vivid details of your lovemaking during
the first six months of your relationship. It's the last six years
that are tricky! After the build-up of yesterday, create new
shared memories of sex that will stay with you both when
you get home and fuel desire when the rut beckons again.
Use the new location to the max. Move mirrors in your hotel
room so that you can see yourselves while you have sex.
Throw your lover against a wall in a tiny cobbled street. Slip
away from the lights and have sex in some secluded place.

Problem: things are just a bit predictable

If getting away is a problem, choose a location where it
will be easy to relax and spend time talking with each
other. Avoid anything that involves a lot of hassle or even
excitement, so forget backpacking through Eastern Europe.
Think quiet auberge in the South of France or luxurious
English country house.

Day 1

Create intimacy. Turn your hotel bedroom into a sensual sanctuary. Take oils and candles from home. Spend a couple of hours bathing, showering and massaging each other before dinner. Don't rush into sex (or if you do, maintain the sensual touching afterwards). Live in the moment. Rediscover each other. Hold hands, maintain eye contact as much as possible. Spend an hour talking about your feelings about work, family, friends and your relationship. Your aim is to make your lover feel cherished and 'listened to'.

Day 2

Break the patterns. Each write down on a piece of paper three things that you'd like. Think about this in advance so you've any props to hand. Take turns to fulfil each other's wishes. If you find this too hard, turn it into a game – and take turns being each other's sex slave.

Turn your hotel bedroom into a sensual sanctuary

Dressing up and staying in

Acting out fantasies takes a bit of practice, but can certainly brighten up an otherwise dull Saturday night.

First, get yourselves in the mood – this can be a bit embarrassing to begin with. Climb into bed and talk dirty to one another. Read from some gentle pornographic books (or stronger stuff, if you like). Share some situations that turn you on mentally; talk through the sort of things you'd like to say or do.

The next obvious step is to pick a night to play out your fantasy, although sometimes it's best just to go for it spontaneously – you'll feel less self-conscious. Even if the first time is a disaster and lasts about 2 minutes before you start laughing, at least you've made a start.

You won't have to expend any money on special outfits (unless you want to), as you can improvise with dressing up and props. Again, it helps if one of you (the one who will be dominant in the fantasy makes the most sense) takes control of organising and briefing the other on their role. Alcohol can help... a lot (though a lot of alcohol will dull the senses). Before you know it, you'll be heading for your local fancy-dress store for your Robin Hood or nun's outfit.

Six clichéd (and that's because they work) fantasy role plays

Doctor and nurse

It's the end of another gruelling day on the wards. The nurse (either one of you) is looking exhausted. The doctor calls the nurse over and says, 'You're looking tired. Could you do with a complete examination?' The doctor gets the examination table ready and asks the nurse to lie down on it. A complete medical later and the diagnosis is 'nervous tension'. However, the doctor is conducting a scientific study into this condition, with some controversial treatment options. If the nurse is willing to take part in some medical experimentation and give feedback on how well the cure works, the doctor will demonstrate the technique...

Master and slave

One of you is the cruel master (or mistress); one is the gorgeous slave. The master is deciding whether to buy or not – which involves a thorough examination. The slave is wrapped in layers of clothes and drapes, but is slowly stripped (or ordered to strip) so the master can confirm that the slave is in good physical condition – and that means that every part of them is in good physical condition. Then, of course, the slave's ability to follow orders and please the master must be tested...

Boss and interviewee

The interviewee comes to the office after hours in one fantasy. Another idea; to be interviewed for their dream job. The interview starts off normally: the interviewee is anxious to please and the interviewer is gracious. However, when they start to discuss terms of employment, some of the terms are quite unusual. Late-night working? Threesomes with the head of personnel and the boss? Finally, there is an initiative test – how well the interviewee performs determines whether or not they get the job...

Husband and the Swedish au pair

He is the innocent, she the fun-loving au pair (extra points if she can keep the accent going all the way through). The wife is away and he's settling down to watch the football when she asks if she can join him. Is he seeing things or is her skirt always that short? And is she sitting a little closer than normal? She seems more flirtatious, more brazen. Double meanings and loaded looks are passing between them. He tries to get a grip of himself and resist temptation while she goes out of her way to seduce him into making the first move. Until finally, losing patience, she makes her intentions quite clear...

Handyman and housewife

He arrives ready for work, but she insists on a cup of tea and a chat first. While she's showing him the problem 'with her pipes', she gets into such a position that he can't help noticing she's not wearing any underwear...

Naughty maid and 'master of the house'

She's supposed to be cleaning the house when the 'master' comes home and discovers her pleasuring herself instead. He's furious and threatens her with dismissal. She is beside herself. Now she has to think of something quick that will persuade him that sacking her is a bad idea...

*Pick a night to play
out your fantasy*

Q and A:
Just imagine…

Having trouble with your fantasy life?
Here are some common problems and solutions.

Q. I think about acting out fantasies, but I feel too self-conscious.

A. Acting out a role that's already predetermined removes performance pressure, so copy some scenes from movies. You'll have a rough dialogue already – what you can remember from the script. For instance, almost anyone can do a duff Scottish accent and an unbelievable Eastern European one, so every couple can get to play James Bond and Bond Girl. If you can persuade him to wear a DJ, even better. What about Jessica Lange and Jack Nicholson in *The Postman Always Rings Twice*? Wander round your kitchen sporting a low cleavage, tight skirt, extremely high heels and a drawl like Blanche Dubois (*A Streetcar Named Desire*) on a pint of bourbon. After a bit of flirting, he'll be desperate to throw you on the kitchen table and rip your clothes off. Just like the movie.

Q. Our home doesn't exactly lend itself to acting out fantasies. How can we set the scene?

A. Lighting helps. Make sure you have low-key lighting, whether from candles, a pin torch or a low lamp, whatever is appropriate for the fantasy. But this doesn't have to be an Oscar-winning production. The main thing is to get rid of any clutter, especially the kids' toys and any photos of your mother. Remove anything that even the world's most active imagination would balk at finding during sex.

Q. It's fine for a special occasion, but you can't keep this sort of thing up all the time. Then the lovey-dovey feelings go and it's back to business as usual. How can we keep that lovin' feeling?

A. Make 'change for change's sake' your mantra in every aspect of your life together. This serves to make you more spontaneous with each other. For instance, moving the position of your bed can subconsciously remind you to keep things fresh in the bedroom, as can something so simple as swapping sides of the bed. Who made the rule that he always sleeps on the left? Do you always eat dinner at the table? Then have a picnic in front of the TV.

Does one of you take responsibility for cleaning the car? Then the other one should do it for a month. If you're constantly making small, subtle changes in your everyday life, you'll automatically bring this into the bedroom – or onto the kitchen table if you're really entering into the spirit of things. When change is an everyday part of your life, it's easier to suggest something new sexually to your partner.

Q. It's difficult for us to get time to spark up our sex life. What can we do?

A. Few people have reasons so genuine for avoiding sex that they can't find a way past them if they're motivated enough. If you're not sufficiently motivated, that's your problem. Talk about it first.

Fantasy destinations

There are some fabulous places
to have sex – and you don't have
to get a babysitter!

Doing it differently is one of the foundations for constantly exciting sex. Every so often, make one of your dates an at-home soirée. Decide on your fantasy destination – use your imagination and introduce as much role-play as you feel comfortable with.

A fantasy destination is great fun. It's a cheap game and it gets your creative juices flowing. How many classic/clichéd love scenes can you re-enact without leaving your house? Here are some ideas to get you going.

The top five fantasy destinations

An alpine lodge in a blizzard (your living room)
It's winter; deep winter. You are two climbers who've had to take shelter in a remote log cabin, cut off from the rest of the world and locked fast by a blizzard. You've no electricity, little food but luckily lots of brandy.

You spread a blanket in front of the log fire, light a couple of candles and sip at your brandy. Outside the wind is howling. Your fellow climber looks more attractive by the minute. And then he suggests a game of poker – which soon becomes strip poker. Except it's chilly with no clothes on and soon you're wondering how you can persuade him to get under the blanket (or better still, into a very cosy sleeping bag) and huddle together for warmth.

Working late at the office (your kitchen)

One of you is the boss. The boss has very high standards and expects a great deal from their assistant. The assistant is working late one night (at your kitchen table posing as a desk), bent over their work with only a desk lamp for illumination. Suddenly, the boss strides in and throws a sheaf of papers at the hapless assistant's head and lets loose with a stream of invective along the lines of, 'This is rubbish. If you want to keep your job, you're going to have to be punished until you do it better.'

The hapless assistant is tied up to a chair while the boss begins to undress the assistant and himself then hisses, 'You'd like to touch me, but you're so incompetent you wouldn't know what to do with it.' The boss then proceeds to show the assistant how it should be done, ordering the assistant to help make amends for past mistakes.

The sauna (your bathroom)

It's very hot and steamy (thanks to your shower being on full). In fact, it's so steamy at first you don't notice that someone else is sharing the sauna with you. Then you see a figure sitting close by, wrapped in a white towel. You smile uncertainly, then shut your eyes and relax, letting the steam overwhelm you. You open your eyes. Your companion is staring at you. Their towel falls open. Everyone is supposed to wear swimsuits but you never do, and obviously they don't either.

You're embarrassed. Do you ignore it for a while, and if you do, what will they do next? Should you point out that their towel has slipped, or just to be polite, let your own slip a little too…?

The camping holiday (your garden, in summer)
You've gone on a holiday – walking in the hills. After a long day, you set up camp (or settle under the stars in your sleeping bags) in the middle of nowhere. Then a handsome stranger happens to come by. You switch on a torch, have some dinner, share a few jokes, drink some wine, start to talk about sexual experiences you've had and some you'd like to try. Soon it's time to turn into your tent. The stranger sleeps outside.

You lie in bed, fantasising about him, waiting breathlessly for him to open the flap of your tent. Or if you simply can't wait (and the possibility of the neighbours watching adds another thrill), you creep out under the stars.

Murder in the dark (your house, with the lights off)
You're both guests at a country-house party. A fellow guest has suggested a game of murder in the dark. One of you goes off to hide somewhere in the dark silent house. The other is the murderer, who stealthily hunts them down, getting closer and closer. But when the murderer finds the victim, there's another surprise for both of them...

Make one of your dates an at-home soirée

Think kink…

Remember: we don't always get
what we want… But we can always ask.

Your mission, should you choose to accept it, is to ask your partner to try something you're convinced has never occurred to them. This idea is a generic 'how to' on asking for anything you might want to try in bed – or indeed, out of it.

Stating the obvious

If you want to try something out of the norm, then you'll have to communicate it to your lover either verbally or physically.

1. First, butter them up by faking a crisis of confidence. Tell them you're worried they'll leave you – couples are splitting up everywhere (give examples). Do this in a light-hearted manner over a bottle of wine or in a worried way after faking moodiness that has them wondering what's wrong. Tell them that although your love life is fine, you feel you've been complacent and you don't want them to get bored. Modify this basic script depending on your lover's gullibility levels, but you get the idea: make it your problem, not theirs. And then introduce some changes into your love life.

2. Once you've mixed it up a little and you're regularly trying new things, suggest a modest first step on the way to

what you want. If you'd like them to whip you with a cat o' nine tails, then suggesting you experiment with a little mild pain via dripping candle wax might be a good start. Just remember to have a safe signal so you know when to stop if it's getting too much and only do what both of you are comfortable with.

3. Work up to the real deal. Be patient: six months' patient, if necessary.

Never forget…

The secret to persuading your lover to do something kinky that you want (and they aren't particularly interested in) is to make it clear that it's them doing the kinky thing that you're interested in, not the act itself. Use imagination, tact and flattery to find a way to make this obvious. Remember, the secret is always to make your lover feel special and to convince them how important they are to you, so go gently.

Make your lover feel special

Danger!

No kidding, it's the fastest-acting aphrodisiac and it works better than porn!

In a famous experiment, an attractive scientist interviewed two groups of men. The first group had a standard interview, while the second was interviewed after they'd crossed a particularly dangerous rope bridge. By the time they were interviewed, their palms were sweaty and their hearts beating fast. This group of men found the same interviewer significantly more alluring – the danger had heightened their sexual response.

In another experiment, male volunteers were each assigned an attractive female assistant. They were informed the experiment was investigating electric shock treatments. Some men were told they were in the control group so they wouldn't be receiving shocks. The rest were advised they would receive painful jolts of electricity. Then they were asked how attracted they felt to their research partner. The ones nervously awaiting the shocks found the same women significantly more attractive than the control group.

If you want thrills, get scared together. It's a caveman thing. Share danger together and the guy has the opportunity to look after the female, and she gets to feel all fragile and protected – even if she's a cut-throat investment banker!

No one's suggesting you set yourself up for anything life-threatening, but sharing adventures together will do the job – especially physical adventures. Adventures count as anything that gets your adrenaline flowing. Seek out a shared experience that gets both your hearts thumping.

Some ideas to get you started

Soft core
- Go to Disneyland or anywhere with fast, high rides.
- Dare each other.
- Have sex where you might just be seen.
- Stay the night somewhere reputedly haunted but definitely creepy.
- Shop at a sex store together.

Hard core
- Have sex where other people could definitely see you. Be subtle, though – you don't want to frighten the horses or get arrested.
- Go white-water rafting, bungee- or parachute jumping.
- Take your clothes off at midnight at the end of your street.
- Go to amateur night at your local comedy club together. Stand up and be funny.

Seek out a shared experience that gets both your hearts thumping

Time to get real?

Actively trying to instil a sense of danger to your lives should act as an aphrodisiac, but to strengthen the bond between you both (and not just the sexual energy), look at the totality of the life you're building together. If you're experiencing sexual doldrums, is this because your life has become stale and everything's routine? As a couple, are you building the sort of life you want? Is it time to stop playing at being dangerous and start taking some genuine risks with the intention of improving your life? Maybe it's time to move to the country, move to the city, move jobs, have a child, adopt a child, travel round the world, give up work and live off the land, start a new business or live on a beach. Sure, it's frightening and of course it might backfire but if you can agree on an enormous life-changing, scary-as-hell decision together and you succeed, your satisfaction with each other should be sky-high. And there's nothing like feeling you've worked hard and succeeded at something with your soulmate to give your libido a bit of a boost.

Four

Making a good thing better

Because there's always room
for a little improvement.

Play away

**Sex toys aren't called that for nothing.
They're fun... great fun!**

Every couple should have their own treasure chest – a special, locked box into which they can dip for a little inspiration. But what to put in it? Just go shopping. It makes a great date. You might want to go virtual shopping, which is more discreet – and if you get on the Net now you might be playing with your new toy within forty-eight hours. Here are some ideas.

Lube

…And loads of it. Using lube doesn't mean you're not a hot vixen. It makes everything better, especially if you want a good long session.

Lush is a slightly cheaper version of the famous Liquid Silk, while Probe is a great lubricant for those with allergies. Escalate contains L-arginine, a natural substance that encourages blood flow and increases sexual pleasure. L-arginine is terrific, but it's not recommended for herpes sufferers as there's a small chance it may aggravate.

If you rely on latex products for contraception, don't use Vaseline, baby oil or anything else that will eat up the rubber.

Dildos and strap-ons

Around a third of strap-ons are sold to heterosexual couples. Straight men are getting in touch with their prostates.

Whatever your persuasion, look out for slip-on harnesses, such as a neat Velcro G-string that gives a snugger fit than many other harnesses, so no flapping about.

There are so many different types of dildos, but the serious choice is silicone. Though expensive, it feels great and quickly heats to your body temperature.

Rear action

Butt plugs don't provide any motion but they give your anal muscles something to react against when you come. If you like repeated contraction and relaxation of these same muscles then try some beads. Whipped out slowly, or all at once at the point of orgasm, they give the prostate a great workout. And, of course, you can buy long thin vibrators specially designed for anal stimulation.

Consider this…

Look for sex toys made of quality materials such as silicone and Pyrex glass and ones that incorporate new technology into the designs.

Some men might feel intimidated by a huge dildo, but they're less likely to be intimidated by products that don't even look like a sex aid. The Fresh Vibes range (www.funfactory.de) has an animal design incorporated into the length. Spokeswoman Jill-Evelyn Hellwig explains: 'Many of our customers are women with children and they need something that's not going to be problematic if their children come across it.' Try a clitoral massager like the Fun Factory Layaspot, which simply sits over your pubic bone and hums away. With different speeds and programmes to vary the tempo, you can also keep it in place while you have sex with your partner (he'll share a bit of the thrill too).

Specially curved toys also make it easier to find your G-spot. It's simpler to turn off your vibrator, or use a dildo to find it first (generally the other end will be designed to tickle your clitoris to give you double stimulation). G-toys are the most problematic to fit as women's vagina length varies. There are a lot of toys out there, so experiment to find out what works for you.

Every couple should have their own treasure chest

More orgasms guaranteed

Is there a scientific way to increase
your chances of coming during penetrative sex?
The answer's yes... two, in fact.

Many women need a lot of clitoral stimulation but traditional sexual techniques often stimulate the vaginal area more, leaving some women extremely frustrated. To remedy this, the CAT (Coitally Adjusted Technique) was invented in the 90s in the USA and it's specifically designed for extra clitoral stimulation. Start off in the basic missionary position with your partner resting his full weight on your chest. Now manoeuvre until you're lying with both pelvic bones touching. That way, he can ride higher than normal (his head will be around 15 cm further up the bed), most of his penis is out of your vagina, but the head will be pressed alluringly against your clitoris.

Wrap your legs around him – this allows him to penetrate you more deeply – and hold on tightly to each other. Now you both rock together, keeping your pelvises tight against each other, avoiding thrusting movements: there's no in-and-out action with this one. The idea is to rock gently to a climax.

Women have 50% more chance of climaxing in this position and the non-thrusting aspect of it makes him less likely to come. It's also a good position for coming at the same time.

In their book, *The Big O*, Dr David Delvin and Christine Webber claim to have invented the aptly named PUSSY (Penis Underneath Scientifically Situated Yoni) position. Simply an upside-down variation of the CAT, this time he gets to lie flat and you lower yourself onto the first part of his penis only. Your hips and chin should be below his and you'll bend his penis so that it stimulates your clitoris once again. Aim for clitoral/penis contact and once again grind away.

When doing this one, take care not to bend his penis too far the wrong way! Don't forget that you can also improve clitoral stimulation by applying lots of lube first, moving more and using longer strokes; also by finding better ways to position yourself. For instance, try props like a chair, specially designed wedges or a sling, all of which assist in getting the optimum angle.

Increase your chances of coming during penetrative sex

Study the Kama Sutra positions and you'll see that, simply by moving the position of your pelvis or legs, you can find a huge variety of positions without too much difficulty. Your legs can be straight, higher, curled on his chest or he can lean forward and you can both squeeze with your thighs to produce the pressing position.

Flirt!

Whether you're single or you've been with a partner for what seems like forever, flirting in a general way with everyone – male or female – makes you more charming, gets you attention and boosts your sexual confidence. Ultimately that feeds into your experience in bed.

Flirting is simply about feeling upbeat, smiling and using body language that conveys positive emotions. In The Flirt Coach *Petra Heskell says about flirting: 'It is simply about feeling great about who you are and spreading it to other people which makes them feel great too.'*

The crucial way to flirt is to use your eyes more. If you're in a social situation, glance about the room and let your eyes linger on the people you find interesting. Be careful, though, as eye contact is such a powerful way to communicate. If someone returns your interest – or even better, smiles – then you can feel more confident that they're already interested when you eventually do approach them.

'There are times not to flirt. When you're sick. When you're with children. When you're on the witness stand.'
Joyce Jillson, author

If you've looked at a group of men, don't be afraid to approach all of them. Say something like, 'Has anyone got the time?' and if one of them is interested, he'll make it clear. Don't worry about your opening line – more attention will be focused on your body language (55%) than what you actually say (7%). If he wants the conversation to continue, he'll show it.

People who like each other have more eye contact than those who don't and tend to stand closer together. When we initiate conversation, it's likely to be in the personal zone (45–122 cm), but during a conversation you might draw closer together into the intimate zone (15–45 cm). If things get really personal, and you start whispering in each other's ear – the close intimate zone (0–15 cm) – it's normally for a special reason.

Even if you're avoiding getting too close or keeping your distance, you'll know the conversation's going well when your partner's body language mirrors your own. It's also easier to get closer to someone when you're sitting side by side, as you might at a bar for instance, than face to face. Look out for body language which is at odds with the facial gestures and words people use, as the body always betrays what's really going through their mind.

'Flirting is a zestful, invigorating pastime. It is the mental equivalent of doing twenty push-ups and jogging five miles, since a good flirt must use her brain about three times normal speed.'
Cynthia Heimel, author

Be contrary

Put your love life in reverse gear. If you avoid
sex, chase it. If there's a position you love, don't
do it. Courting frustration could be just the trip
you need to drive you over the edge.

Being intimate is a double-edged sword. Sometimes it brings you too close and you need to be a little more ruthless sexually to enjoy getting off. Over time it's almost inevitable for a couple's sex life to decrease in frequency. Often we're simply unrealistic about our sexual expectations because our culture is saturated with images of sex and romantic longing. We feel we should want more, and this unfocused yearning can lead to us seeking out affairs. It's possible to be in an endless cycle of falling in love, getting disillusioned, meeting someone else and repeating the whole cycle. Elizabeth Taylor once described herself as 'addicted to love'.

In reality what we have to deal with most when we grapple with sexual problems is our own psyche. During sex we must open ourselves up to our vulnerabilities. We all carry insecurities that have been with us from childhood and at first a new sexual liaison gives us a chance to work against this. If a woman has grown up feeling physically inferior to her beautiful mother, initially she might take refuge in a relationship with an especially attractive man. Over time, however, her old insecurities will emerge and return to plague her, and this is why so many couples start to experience sexual problems after the honeymoon period, which were not at first apparent.

Some couples say they have less sex but it's more intimate; however, this too has its own problems. The more intimate you become, the more you're aware of your partner's frailties. Psychotherapist Dr Michael Bader says in *Arousal: The Secret Logic of Sexual Fantasies*, 'As couples get to know each other, their deeper awareness of each other's vulnerabilities can become their undoing. The other's inhibitions and the shame upon which they rest begin to wear down spontaneity and passion. We are just too close, too identified with our inhibited partner, to escape the experience.' It's important to have a certain degree of sexual ruthlessness and sometimes we all need some kind of emotional distance (via fantasy or physical space) to be able to switch off and concentrate on our own sexual needs.

If your sex life is nothing to write home about, deliberately try to avoid it for a while. When something's on tap, you can both take it for granted. See how long the two of you can go without having sex. It's a good idea not to stop all physical activity: you could try masturbating separately and telling each other all about it when you do come together. The idea is to get you hot, but you can still agree on whether to postpone sex or not – maybe when you eventually succumb to passion it'll be even better. Sometimes being frustrated, that feeling of suppressed longing, leads to the best sex of all so it's worth waiting until you just can't hold back any longer.

To objectify your partner a little, try playing around with sexual fantasy. Have him dress up a little differently or speak to you in bed in a different voice. The aim is to think of him erotically, as a means to give you great sex, rather than a soul-mate with lots of problems to talk over. Over time we can desexualise our partners, so now's the chance to inject some throbbing desire into the proceedings. It could be that he's treating you gently when you really want to be ravaged, so try talking dirty and see if this makes it easier for you to get excited.

Being intimate is a double-edged sword

Keeping it fresh: the experts' guide

'An orgasm with your spouse once a week is the secret to love.'
Ava Cadell, 12 Steps to Everlasting Love

'Eliminate all distractions for 20 minutes a day, and give 100% of your attention to each other.'
Jerry Larson, The Great Marriage Tune-up Book

'Listen to phone messages on speaker phone. Tell your spouse all your passwords. Putting these private matters out in the open allows real trust.'
Judy Kuriansky, The Complete Idiot's Guide to A Healthy Relationship

Surprise!

Isn't it time you got in touch
with your creative side?

Laura Corn, author of *101 Nights of Grrreat Sex*, has based her considerable best-selling success on one simple concept: the importance of the surprise factor. Each of her 101 suggestions depends on the fact that your partner doesn't have a clue what sexual delight you're planning.

It's a clever gimmick, and it works. Surprise your lover sexually every week for a year and you can bet your bootee you won't be collecting any 'boring in bed' prizes. Encouraging the element of surprise in your sex life keeps you young and playful, makes you feel cherished and appreciated; and keeps your lover crazy for you. Do something slightly different every time you make love. Throw in an element of surprise. After a few weeks, mixing it up becomes second nature and the payoff makes it all worthwhile.

Why surprise works

A little bit of effort to surprise your lover with a new technique, seduction, outfit or behaviour reaps huge improvements. As long as it's something unexpected, the surprise can be whatever you like. It can be filthy, funny, sweet and romantic or even more embarrassing than karaoke night down your local.

Some of your surprises will be easy to organise; others may take more planning. You might spend an hour (or more) setting up a gorgeous seduction for your mate – a lot of work – but he'll remember it for the rest of his life. But even more unforgettable for your mate than the great sex you'll enjoy is how loved they'll feel. Men, just as much as women (in fact, if psychologists are to be believed, even more than women), are delighted by the proof that someone wants them so much that they'll put extra thought and effort into their seduction. All of us love to feel special.

It takes both of you to commit to the idea. You'll only want to put effort into thrilling your partner if you feel they're going to make the same effort for you. Not every idea will work, but there has to be an agreement that neither of you can fail; even the ones that don't work are not to be laughed at or sneered at. Hopefully the failures will draw you closer and just thinking about the successes will energise your love life for years to come.

Surprise your lover sexually every week for a year

Surprise ideas

On your next date, you can keep your coat on. Well, you don't want the whole restaurant to know you're naked underneath, just him!

Buy half a case of his favourite wine (a dozen bottles is classier but might be too much of a demand on your imagination). Around the neck of each one, place a sealed envelope containing details of where and when you're going to drink it together. These are IOUs of pleasure. Let your imagination run riot.

One night when you're getting amorous in a lovey-dovey sort of way, suddenly flip personality and change the whole atmosphere. From Dr Jekyll to Mr Hyde. Stop smiling, get mean. Tie his wrists, blindfold him… Now you can do whatever you like.

Spend an hour or so pleasuring him sensually, such as oral sex, washing his hair, applying body lotion to every inch of his skin or holding him and stroking his hair until he falls asleep. Don't allow him to do a thing for you in return.

In search of the G-spot

Those who've found their G-spot think it's well worth searching for.

The G-spot is the female equivalent of the male prostate and, with a little tender loving care, it provides terrific sensations, culminating in a great orgasm. To begin with, it's easiest to find it on your own. First, squat and have a feel. The G-spot is situated on the front of the vaginal wall, about a third to halfway towards the cervix, a few inches inside. It feels slightly rough and is about a couple of centimetres across. Still struggling? Feel for something that's more of a ridge than round.

Pressing on the G-spot will feel spongy because what you're feeling through the skin of the vaginal wall is the insulation that surrounds the urethra, which carries urine from your bladder to the outside world. The insulating sheath includes multiple glands that swell during sexual excitement; when stimulated in the right way, they will spurt out a clear fluid that emerges through the urethra just like pee. This is totally different in composition from pee and is, in fact, the so-called female ejaculate.

Men who want to float their partner's love boat with some G-spot action might find using a finger rather than their penis is a lot less tiring. You may have to go quite fast but if she likes the idea of this, ask her to demonstrate first or you could do her damage. Have your partner sit or lie facing you, insert your index finger and repeatedly press firmly. Also, try hooking your finger slightly as if beckoning and press repeatedly on the G-spot.

When it comes to the act itself, remember that shallow penetration is the only kind that works and imagine you're aiming for the navel. Rear entry positions are best; the 'spoon', where you both lie on your sides with him behind her, is easiest on both of you. Nothing happening? Try a vibrator specifically designed to hit the G-spot. Women may feel the need to pee during these manoeuvres, as stimulating the G-spot means you're pressing on the urethra. But stick with it, as it means you're getting close.

Is it worth it? Nearly all women enjoy having attention paid to the anterior wall of the vagina because of the huge number of nerve endings there. Becoming aware of how they react to different kinds of stimulation – manual, penile and plastic – can only improve your sexual repertoire of sensations. Just don't get hung up on it. Women don't need another body part to become neurotic about!

Improve your sexual repertoire of sensations

Quiz:
How smart are you about sex?

Developing sexual intelligence makes sex a lot more enjoyable.

1. What does sex mean for you?
a) Affection, comfort.
b) Passion or love, intimacy or comfort – different things at different times.

2. Most times you have sex…
a) You'll both please each other.
b) It will be different each time. You use sex as an expression of what's going on between you.

3. You expect to have sex with your partner…
a) When he asks you.
b) When you are both in the mood.

4. Your partner asks you to do something new in bed…
a) You feel you should say yes, but feel a bit threatened.
b) You're prepared to talk about it until you feel confident enough.

5. You're having a 'fat day' and your man wants sex. You…
a) Do what you can to avoid it.
b) Let him persuade you how beautiful you are.

Mostly As

You seem to be an enthusiastic partner but you think more of what your partner wants than your own needs. Eventually this will backfire. Look at any outstanding issues around sex and work out what you want from it… then go for it!

Mostly Bs

You are a confident lover. You're in touch with your feelings and use sex as another way of showing how you feel about your partner. You are realistic – sex won't always be brilliant. And if it's not, you know that with good communication you can fix it.

Full body contact

What you can do with your tongue is limited, and most of us master the different variations of giving oral sex – long slow licks, flicking action, focused pressure on hot spots, etc. – pretty early on.

The magic lies in what you can do with the rest of your body while you're licking and generally pleasuring him with your mouth. Incorporate the principles of kaizen (small changes causing big differences) into your blow-job technique. It's during oral sex more than just about anything else that we tend to stick to the same pattern, over and over again. And for good reason: if it works, why throw away a winning formula? But try mixing it up just a little and you can take what's already pleasurable into the realms of a mind-blowing experience.

Hands

Touch his chest; squeeze his nipples.

Put the fingers of one hand in his mouth so he can suck and lick them.

Trace around his anus, balls and perineum (the space between the first two) with your fingers.

Slip a well-lubricated finger into his bum and stimulate the prostate gland – which you can feel through the skin of the anterior wall (front), with gentle pressure. Give him plenty of warning first that this is your intention. If he doesn't like this, press rhythmically on the perineum, which stimulates the prostate more gently.

Hold tight onto his buttocks and spread the cheeks – many men, like women, appreciate the sense of 'stretch'.

Push up the fleshy area just above his pubic bone or press on it rhythmically. This increases the sensations you're causing with your mouth.

Put one hand on the base and another halfway up the penis. Stroke the penis with both hands while you take the head of it in your mouth.

Use a vibrator or a bullet on low speed on his perineum while you fellate him.

Eyes

It's oh so simple but if you don't usually look into your lover's eyes when you go down on him, give this a go. A locked gaze while your mouth slides up and down is powerfully erotic.

Legs

Straddle his chest as an alternative to the more usual blow-job positions and go on all fours, if necessary. This leaves you exposed, but visually it's pretty damn exciting – especially if you touch yourself while going south! This also allows him to touch you without any effort whatsoever, which is nice for him.

Rhythm

Ultimately you'll find a technique he likes, a groove that he enjoys and you'll stick to it. At the most, alternate between two techniques. The only exception to this is when you want to prolong things, which can ensure a stronger, better orgasm for him. Not always, however. Some men's penises appear to get tired of a constant stop–start, stop–start method and their orgasm isn't half as explosive as sex manuals would have you believe so unless you know your man, don't overdo the teasing.

Straddle his chest as an alternative to the more usual blow-job positions

Deep-throat – fact or fiction?

According to some people, deep-throating doesn't exist – and certainly not in the way it does in the 70s film starring Linda Lovelace since no woman has a clitoris on the back of her throat nor should she expect multi-orgasms when she goes down. Lots of us get a real sense of power and enjoyment from oral sex, though – and if you don't, it would be worth working out why.

In fact, deep-throating (in the sense of taking the whole length of a man's penis into your mouth) is possible and there's no big mystique to it. It's simply a matter of controlling your gag reflex and this might take some practice. You should be in control of his penis, with your hand on the base so that you can be quite sure of this. Keep working up and down, taking his penis into your mouth, a bit at a time. When it hits the back of your throat, the secret is to get the hang of the breathing. Breathe in as the penis leaves the back of your throat and out when it hits the back of your throat. Go a little further each time. Once you are expert at taking his entire length into your mouth, you can experiment with positions. As a rule of thumb, though: never, ever base your performance on what you see in porn.

Lots of us get a real sense of power and enjoyment from oral sex

'Let a woman be a woman and man be a man'

It turns out that the artist formerly known as Prince had a point. In fact, there's an American called David Deida with some interesting, if old-fashioned suggestions on how to improve your love life. There's nothing particularly new about his ideas, but the way he packages his theories is pretty compulsive.

We're equal, but we're exhausted. Even long-standing relationships crumble under the strain of couples overworking. Latest figures show that the divorce rate is inching towards half of all marriages. But, according to Deida, life doesn't have to be this way. He says women aren't drudges but passionate, vital, thrilling creatures; given the chance, they should be living a life of rich emotional complexity. In order to shine, they need the love of what Deida calls 'the superior man' – in other words, a strong, focused, individual striving towards his destiny. According to Deida, when men are strong and women can rely on them, passionate intensity isn't far away. What's wrecking our sex lives, he says, is too much equality.

'The bottom line of today's fifty–fifty relationship,' he continues, 'is that men and women are clinging to a politically correct sameness even in bed and that's when sexual attraction disappears. The love may be strong, but the sexual polarity fades.' According to Deida, men and women have both a masculine and feminine side (or 'polarity'). It's fine for men to get in touch with their feminine side (real men do cry), and women with their masculine side (they're brilliant in the boardroom). She can be the breadwinner, he can look after the kids, but if they want fireworks to continue he has to be someone she can rely on and trust, and she must remove the shoulder pads as soon as she walks through the front door.

So, what's a 'superior man'?

Deida's roots appear to be in the men's movement (the reaction to feminism), which tries to help men make sense of our crazy, mixed-up world – and their role in it. He believes a man isn't really happy unless he's striving towards his goal, whatever that is. When he loses sight of his goal, he needs 'time out' – something that in other cultures would have been called a 'vision quest'. Metaphorically speaking, it means going into the desert and beating his drum until he finds his way again. And unless he finds his way, he's no use to anyone – least of all you.

Feel good now: *Lie in bed, 'spooned' around one another and simply breathe in unison. Try this once a day, in bed or out, clothed or not. Hold onto each other and regulate your breaths. Let thoughts drift away as they float into your mind – just be with each other. This improves communication and builds up intimacy.*

A man who knows his way is a superior man and you can help yours to get there by 'challenging him', i.e. not putting up with any nonsense. No lying about watching Sky Sports when he should be looking for a job, say. No nights down the pub to distract him from the fact that he hasn't written a word of that best-selling novel. Though Deida calls it 'challenging', it could easily be confused with nagging, so go gently!

And what about the 'superior woman'?

No, it's not about giving up your job and getting back in the home. Or agreeing with everything he says. Couples can switch polarity completely, and as long as that works for you and the polarity is present, fine. But most of us switch between polarities and the danger lies when a woman is expected to carry too much of the masculine energy and can't switch back into being feminine. These days, who can doubt that many women are dazed and confused, attempting to do too much and taking their frustrations out on their men? Your aspirations are important, too. But for your relationship's sake, maintain polarity and keep in touch with your 'sense of identity'.

A woman should nourish her femininity at every opportunity – dancing, music, yoga, hanging out with girlfriends, orgasmic sex. All of these will support your feminine essence and making time for them should be a priority if you want your relationship to stay strong. Do some nourishing every day. Have a long luxurious bath, dress in silk or other sensuous fabric, massage with scented oils, play your favourite music and dance like no one's watching, or stare at the stars. Spend as much time as possible with supportive women friends – often they can see what you need better than you yourself can. And before you ask… yes, your partner has to actively help you find time for these things. That's the superior way.

Support your feminine essence

Are you sexually mature?

Because it *is* big and it *is* clever! It's easy to keep sex vibrant at the beginning of any relationship, but how do you keep it hot for longer?

Men and women may enjoy casual sex in much the same way, but when it comes to the long haul – the big relationship where the expectations and desire of each partner is that it lasts for the foreseeable future – different attitudes towards what constitutes closeness can develop over the years. Generalising like crazy, women seem to show their love through emotional closeness and need their partner to demonstrate that he loves them through emotional closeness – talking, discussion, showing empathy. On the whole, however, men tend to show their love through physically doing something – earning money, cleaning the car, sexual contact. Sex, not discussion, is their way of showing love and feeling loved.

Frequently, men don't place enough value on emotional contact and women don't place physical contact highly enough. That's fine when things are going well, when both partners 'put out' for each other, but if a change happens in their lifestyle and one partner withdraws the contact the other needs, a vicious cycle ensues. He's not encouraged to extend emotional closeness to her while she withdraws physical contact from him. In turn, she cannot understand how he can expect her to have sex when they're barely grunting at each other and he spends entire evenings watching TV. At best, their sex life is mediocre, sporadic and unsatisfying – and it stays that way.

This is the pattern of the sexually immature couple. They may once have had a great sex life, they may have a lot of sexual history but sexual experience has nothing to do with sexual maturity.

When you're sexually mature…

You don't wait for sex to just happen

No, you make sex a priority. You go to work when you're tired; you may call your mother when you're stressed. You feed the kids when you have a headache… Sexually mature couples allow sex the same priority they give to other important aspects of their lives. They remain open to the idea of having sex at any time; they trust their lover will find a way to turn them on.

You know the importance of doing it differently

Not least because your relationship, your body and your life won't stay the same. Being prepared to alter the way you have sex prepares you for the inevitable changes that will occur in your life. It's something that brings you respite when life gets messy, joy when life sometimes becomes dreary, and comforts you when illness or death leave their scars on your psyche. Sex with your loving partner is a place you can go when you want to celebrate life's happiness, and it's also somewhere you can run to hide from life's hurts.

You use sex to show your partner they're loved

Reaching out to your partner helps you to avoid passive–aggressive games. You don't let just one person always initiate sex because that means the other has the power to refuse or withdraw. Sex can become a punishment or reward, and if this is your relationship, it's a dangerous place to be because both of you will end up hostile or resenting each other for different reasons.

You actively think of how you can use your sexuality to make your partner happier

This isn't just about giving your partner orgasms. Sex is a gift. You sometimes do stuff for no reward. Lots of people find it really difficult to make a gift of themselves. Even when they push themselves to sexual extremes in an effort to keep the spark between them alive, their relationship just isn't intimate enough to maintain all the emotional intensity that scary sex throws up.

And finally, you try for each other

Each day, you keep coming out to bat for your relationship and actively work to make it more loving. Now that's the way to keep your sex life fresh.

Use sex to show your partner they're loved

Index

The Feel Good Factory on Great Sex